Shining the Light on All the Right

Celebrating the Art of Nursing Around the World

Mark and Bonnie Barnes
Co-founders of The DAISY Foundation

with Jim Eber

Published by Scooter Publishing
Cover Design: Romana Bovan
Interior Design: Eliot House Productions
© 2020 Mark and Bonnie Barnes. All rights reserved.

Library of Congress (LC) Cataloging-in-Publication Data
    Names: Barnes, Mark, author. Barnes, Bonnie, author. Eber, Jim, author (with)
    Title: Shining the light on all the right: celebrating the art of nursing around
       the world
    Description: Scooter Publishing, Marble Falls, Texas, 2020
    Identifiers: LCCN 2019911983 ISBN 978-0-9817789-9-0 (hardback)
    LC record available at https://lccn.loc.gov/2019911983

Printed in the United States of America

To Patrick, whose spirit lifts DAISY

The DAISY Story

An End & A Beginning

"Patrick is in the hospital."............................. 3

Now What Do We Do?
1999–2008

Liquid Dinner 19

Picking the First DAISY............................... 25

Getting It 37

The Healer's Touch................................... 49

A Broken Promise.................................... 59

The Power of Stories and Gratitude 71

Funding Our Future 87

Growing DAISY
2008–2019

What's a Nice Girl Like You 99

We Are Family 109

What Happened to Turnkey?! 119

Shining a New Light 133

All We Wanted to Do Was Say Thank You 147

Facing the Future

Fire 163

Shining the Light on People Who Have
Helped Make DAISY Right

Twenty Years of Gratitude 171

Index 195

An End &
A Beginning

"Patrick is
in the hospital."

That's how the message from Tena started: "Patrick is in the hospital." But he's going to be fine, she said. No need to call. No need to come home from Italy. Enjoy your vacation. We just wanted you to know.

Of course Pat will be fine. He and Tena had welcomed their first child, our first granddaughter, Riley, six weeks earlier. When we saw them after she was born, Pat was more than fine; he was over the moon for Riley. So were we. *Of course Pat will be fine.*

We called anyway.

Tena took us through what had happened. Pat had been pretty tired a few nights before. He turned down dessert, which he never did, and went to bed early. In the middle of the night, he woke up and said, "Something's wrong." He had blood blisters in his mouth and petechiae or small red dots on his arms, stomach, and legs. They thought it looked an allergic reaction, but to what? Whatever it was, it was not normal. They needed to get him to an emergency room. Thankfully, some family was visiting, and they took Pat to Baptist Saint Anthony Medical Center while Tena stayed home with the baby.

At first, the doctors also thought it was an allergic reaction, perhaps to one of the medications Pat took, though none of them had caused any problems before. They took him off his meds and monitored him closely but 24 hours later he wasn't getting better. Meanwhile a blood test had revealed an extremely low platelet count, hence the blood blisters and red dots, as platelets help the blood clot normally. His doctor admitted him to the hospital under the care of the hematologist while they worked on a diagnosis.

There were several possibilities for what was happening, from aplastic anemia to leukemia, and they ran tests for all of them. As Tena listed the possible causes, we were concerned but not panicked, because the doctors had no test results yet and Tena sounded calm. Besides, Pat was resilient. He had already beaten Hodgkin's disease—twice—as an adult. His first diagnosis was during his senior year in college. He still graduated despite missing half the fourth quarter. The second time he beat Hodgkin's, he was 26, not long before he met Tena. He had also recovered just fine from his hip replacement the year before. We—like Tena—resolved to stay positive until there was a reason not to be positive.

Turns out, it wasn't leukemia. Or aplastic anemia. The diagnosis, made almost by process of elimination, was idiopathic thrombocytopenic purpura or ITP. We had never heard of ITP, and neither had Tena, and this being 1999, it wasn't like we could pick up our smartphones and ask Google. Tena had learned all she could from Pat's doctors and what she could find with her Mac and a dial-up modem. None of what she heard or read sounded too scary. The doctors had described ITP as Pat's immune system being "disorganized" and destroying his platelets. No one knows why some people get it or what causes it, they explained, but it affects both children and adults. In children, it usually goes away without treatment or they grow out of it in time. In adults, it's more serious but still treatable. It also can become a chronic condition, so Tena and Pat would need to monitor him after he was treated and sent home.

But Pat wasn't being sent home. ITP usually clears in adults with the first course of treatment: The immune system is suppressed with a course of prednisone to reboot and reorganize it. If the prednisone doesn't work, a second alternate course of treatment typically does. The prednisone didn't work. They were starting the second treatment when Tena sent us the message. But she still didn't want us to worry.

"I'm not worried," Tena said on the phone. "You don't need to come home." We came home.

Tena felt a little guilty cutting our vacation short. What if by the time we got there the second treatment worked and Pat was fine and ready to go home? But he wasn't and she was glad we were there. The family staying with Pat and her had to leave, and they had no one else in Texas who could stay with the baby. With Pat in the ICU with an immune disorder, there was no way she could bring a six-week-old baby with her. She felt alone and grateful for the company, help, and someone to calm her nerves as they treated Our Patrick.

That's what we called him, "Our Patrick." That's what everyone who loved him called him. Patrick was Mark's son from his first marriage. He was an adult when Bonnie met him, yet she felt that connection to him soon after they met. She felt an even deeper connection to Mark, who had been a business associate of hers years before they started dating. In 1996, she retired from a high-level career in advertising in Los Angeles and New York City, moved to Sonoma, and married Mark. With no connections to the region, she spent her days volunteering and learning to grow and tend grapes, converting a few acres from an untamed dog run into a vineyard while Mark continued running his advertising business in San Francisco.

Pat and Tena had ended up in Amarillo because of his job. He started his career in advertising sales working for Mark's company in Los Angeles and then moved to the Atlanta office where he met Tena, who also worked for Mark. Actually, Pat and Tena worked together, and she remembers her first impression of him: "He was a bit of a jerk." Luckily, Pat got a second chance to make a first impression, and it didn't take long for Tena to discover Our Patrick: a funny and fun-loving guy who, having beaten cancer twice, felt lucky to be alive. Mark often says that Pat was a natural salesman. His knowledge of his field and easy way with people served him and his clients well. This extended to his chemotherapy for his second bout with Hodgkin's: He would walk around the unit with his IV pole and visit with other patients, giving them encouragement, telling them it was going to be okay. Pat was a guy who knew no strangers and whose warmth, humor, and outgoing nature made people feel comfortable. He lived each day with gratitude and joy—except when someone cut him off while driving. We knew where Riley would learn her first curse words.

Tena and Pat married in 1994. Soon after, they moved to Memphis where Pat had been offered a job. Then he was offered his first job as a manager in Amarillo. *Amarillo?* Neither he nor we nor anyone in either family had ever been to Amarillo, but we knew the owner of the company offering Pat the job. So when he asked Pat and Tena to visit the city and meet the people in the office, we offered to meet them in Amarillo.

Any one-light-dirt-road-tumbleweed ideas we had about Amarillo were wrong. While Mark and Pat headed to the office, Bonnie drove around with Tena and found a modern city with a great shopping mall, a golf club, movie theaters, a bowling alley, and neighborhoods of lovely homes for Pat and Tena to raise their family in.

Any ideas we had that by the time we got there Patrick would be laid out by something as enigmatic as ITP were similarly wrong. When we made it back to Amarillo from our vacation in Italy, Pat was running his business from his bed. He was so pumped up on prednisone and other medications, he was talking a mile a minute. Make that two miles. Pat usually talked a mile a minute. Looking at him, we initially figured we'd be there for a few days and be back home soon. "I'd give anything to be able to change a diaper," he joked. Our Patrick really seemed to be fine.

Once again, we were wrong. Our Patrick was not fine.

By the time we arrived in Amarillo, the second course of treatment hadn't worked, and we moved in with Tena and the baby, living out of our vacation suitcases. A friend picked up our car at the San Francisco airport. Mark's father was living with us at the time, and he took care of our dogs. Our neighbors watched over them all while we watched over Pat and tried to make sense of his bizarre condition and what the doctors told us.

A third treatment failed. The doctors moved to the next. The nurses counseled us to have patience. Have faith. Let the next treatment do its job. Keep Patrick's spirits high. Not that Pat was having any trouble with that. The nurses weren't going to let whatever this ITP thing was get him down, and neither was he. He engaged each and every one he came in touch with, and they got to know him. When one of his night nurses, Dan, discovered Pat loved sports and that his recall for facts was voluminous, he sat up with Pat on nights he couldn't sleep sparring sports facts, taking his meals with him, and staying late. Mornings after Dan had been up with him, Pat couldn't wait to tell us how he had bested Dan on some arcane sports question.

What Pat was having trouble with was food. A mouth full of blood blisters made eating difficult, and he had very little appetite. Each day we tried to entice him with a different treat he loved. Nothing interested him until the day Mark brought a Cinnabon cinnamon roll to Pat's room for his own breakfast. Pat smelled it and asked for a bite. He proceeded to eat the entire thing and asked us to bring him another the next day. "Be sure to bring enough for all the nurses in the unit too as a thank-you," he said. So we did. And that afternoon, Pat got moved into a VIP room down the hall. Ignoring all rules about correlation and causation, we concluded either they needed Pat's closet-sized room for something more important or that bringing nurses Cinnabon results in being moved to a bigger room with a sofa and big TV. We like to think it was the power of Cinnabon and Patrick. Well, it made sense at the time.

But what Cinnabon and nothing nor anyone had the power to do was make Pat better. The fourth course of treatment failed. As did the fifth, sixth, and seventh courses. They gave him platelet transfusions. Nothing moved the proverbial platelet needle. As Pat worsened, he started to bleed into his lungs and bladder. He struggled to hide the pain and stay positive, as did we.

The doctors began to question if they had the correct diagnosis. They reran all the tests to see if they missed something. They did bone marrow aspirations to make sure his body could still manufacture platelets. It could, but as soon as it did, it attacked and destroyed them. The hospital consulted James George, a physician and ITP specialist from Oklahoma City, who recommended another course of action: a bone marrow transplant. The Amarillo hematologist concurred. "All the signs point to ITP," the doctors told us. "We don't understand why he's not responding. It may be something bigger is going on. A bone marrow transplant would enable him to stop making more antibodies than platelets and start to reverse the course of his condition." The only problem was Baptist St. Anthony's Medical Center didn't do bone marrow transplants, so the doctors recommended two options: MD Anderson Cancer Center at the University of Texas or Fred Hutchinson Cancer Research Center in Seattle.

The choice was an easy one for us: We all wanted to go to Seattle. Fred Hutch had pioneered bone marrow transplants, but more importantly, Patrick was born and raised in the city. His sister was still there and a good enough genetic match for the transplant. His brothers Brad and Adam were also there. So was our dear friend Dianne, who offered her home to all of us, including Tena's mother, one of Tena's friends, and Pat and Tena's beloved golden retriever, Griffey—named for Pat's favorite baseball player on his favorite team: Ken Griffey Jr. of the Seattle Mariners.

The hospital made the arrangements to get Pat to Seattle on an ambulance plane. And for the first time in weeks, instead of worrying, Pat and Tena felt optimistic. "We were actually excited," Tena remembers. "This is it! This is the fix. We know it's a long road, but this is what's going to make him better." We all got swept up in the news and sprang into action. Bonnie said, "I'll fly with him." Mark said he would help Tena pack up the house and get her on the plane with the baby and the dog and then drive Tena's car with all their stuff from Texas to Washington. We were ready to relocate to Seattle for as long as it took to get Pat well.

There was something else to celebrate that day, too: Pat and Tena's fifth anniversary. We thought it would be lovely if we took care of Riley so they could have dinner together. The nurses loved the idea. They found out what his favorite restaurant was and ordered his favored dish: spaghetti dinner. They decorated his room and set everything up. We bought some pearls for Pat to give Tena, picked up dinner, and delivered it all.

Pat and Tena toasted with their water glasses.

"You're going to get better," she said.

"I'm going to get better."

On the plane to Seattle, it was just Patrick, Bonnie, the pilot, and Robert, a nurse from Amarillo. Pat was struggling from the pain and a serious nosebleed, but Robert was unfazed and managed it all in the tiny space with words and limited resources. Robert's priority was keeping Pat comfortable, ensuring that his pain didn't reach a crisis level—which was a real risk as Pat's internal bleeding worsened on the plane—but through it all he also noticed Bonnie's fear and dread and found the time to be compassionate with her. It was at that moment in her mind the nurses went from being "Pat's nurses" to "our nurses."

And our nurses had all they could handle when Pat was admitted to Fred Hutch. His internal bleeding had grown dangerous. He hallucinated that a woman was screaming she needed help and he ripped out his tubes and ran down the hall to save her. By the second night, the bleeding in his lungs had become a real problem. He was having trouble breathing. The doctors called us in the middle of the night to inform us that Pat needed to be put on a ventilator and would need to be put in an induced coma. The three of us got to the hospital at 4:00 A.M.

Before Pat was sedated, he wrote us a note. Five words: *Please don't leave me alone.*

We made sure we kept that promise. We told our nurses about Pat's request, and they were incredibly respectful of it and of us. In fact, they made us part of Patrick's team. No one was ever asked to leave the room when any clinician came in, although we did volunteer to leave during certain procedures. We took the night shift, coming into the hospital at around 7:00 P.M. and leaving as soon as the day shift arrived at 9:00 A.M. or so. The rest of the family and friends shared the daytime. Tena came every moment she could while we helped with the baby at home.

Soon after Pat was intubated, our doctor called a family meeting. He knew the recommendation was that he get a bone marrow transplant, but he told us frankly he wasn't sure Patrick could survive one in his state. He was weak. His body could not fight infection, nor clot blood. The doctor, however, still believed it was ITP and wanted to continue to treat for that, starting an eighth course of treatment for him. The nurses brought in all kinds of new equipment—pumps, monitors, machines. They were totally adept at using and explaining each one to us. ("Okay, this test that we're doing, this is what we're hoping for. This is when we should see some results.") Our nurses warned us not to panic when an alarm sounded on one of the machines. It didn't necessarily mean that Pat was in distress, and they promised to respond quickly to identify the issue. We watched as they studied Pat. They had an expectation of what was right and what was less right, not from looking at the monitors but by watching him. Their judgment was remarkable, and we all were struck by the smallest changes they picked up on and how quickly they responded to them.

The nurses' care for Patrick went beyond the patient and focused on the person. We were moved by the way our nurses touched him. There was a tenderness, a gentleness, an affection for Pat. They asked us to bring in a photo of him, and taped it to the entrance of his room. That way, whenever anyone came in, they were reminded of the vital, healthy, handsome man, son, husband, friend, and new father who was in their care, not the intubated prednisone-swollen man in the induced coma attached to all those tubes and monitors. They asked us what Pat cared about, what he liked to do, what he did for a living. One of our nurses told us that despite the coma he was in, he might well be able to hear us. This nurse shared an experience he had when his father had been sedated after open heart surgery and woke up to recount a family conversation that had taken place at his bedside while he was unconscious. After the nurse told us this story, we stayed positive and upbeat when we were in Pat's room, and everyone heeded our request not to mention in front of Pat that the Seattle Mariners had traded Ken Griffey Jr. to the Cincinnati Reds.

But while our nurses were always focused on Pat, they also focused on us. The doctors were amazing, but they were not always there, and when they were it was sometimes hard to understand and process all they told us. It seemed we always had questions after they left the room or hung up the phone. *What about this? What exactly does that mean? Why did you say that? What happens if . . . ?* We relied on our nurses to answer all these questions and more, fill us in, and explain things in layman's terms. They never made us feel we were asking stupid questions, even though we suspected we were. Nor did they get annoyed if we asked the same question more than once, which we know we did. A lot.

The more nurses educated and involved us, the less helpless we felt, but as with Pat, the nurses went beyond the clinical to get to know us, too. They made sure we were eating and getting some sleep during the day. They asked what Riley was doing as they looked at her pictures that covered Pat's room. They made sure they got to know Tena too, even though she was home most of the time taking care of Riley, who could not visit her dad and be exposed to any kind of infection. The closest Riley got to him was before we left Amarillo. Tena drove alongside the hospital, and our nurses got Pat to the window where Tena held Riley up so he could see her. It was a bit of a metaphor for Tena's whole situation: feeling painfully torn between

Pat and Riley, always feeling on the outside. So we put a sign on the wall of Pat's room so she would never be or feel left out by anyone: TENA'S IN CHARGE.

We learned just how much our nurses knew about us during the night that Pat first involuntarily extubated his ventilator. Given the amount of blood in his lungs, it went flying everywhere as the tube came out. It was the most upsetting thing we had ever seen or experienced. Our nurse that night was Tana, a seasoned, confident clinician who no doubt had been through this kind of thing hundreds of times. Nothing was too dramatic, scary, or critical to throw her. At least that's how it seemed to us when we screamed our heads off calling for her. She appeared instantly and took control of the situation. She knew Mark has a hard time seeing blood, so she threw him out of the room so he wouldn't faint. Then she put Bonnie to work, knowing that she would need to help in some way—to *do something*. In no time, Tana had the ventilator back in place, Bonnie had helped clean Patrick up, and Mark was back in the room and breathing.

Tana left to awaken the resident to report what had happened, while we just sat there completely shaken. When she returned to the room, she came right over to Bonnie and wrapped her arms around her. Then she did the same to Mark. If we didn't know it before, then we sure knew it then: Nurses give the best hugs. And we would need every one of them and more over the next weeks.

Sometimes the hugs were literal, sometimes figurative. One morning, a nurse named Karen saw Bonnie in the hallway waiting for Mark so they could leave after a rough night. She looked at Bonnie: Ghostly remains of yesterday's makeup covered her face, her eyes red and bleary. She asked Bonnie if she would be seeing Tena when we got home. "Yes," Bonnie answered, "she will no doubt be up with Riley." Karen nodded. "Bonnie, I hate to say this to you but if you go home to Tena looking like you're looking? She's gonna think he died. You just can't do that. I need you to go into the bathroom and wash your face. Please put some makeup on. Put some lipstick on. Put in your contact lenses. I don't want Tena to see you this way." Then she gave Bonnie a real hug.

Bonnie couldn't believe Karen had the guts to say that to her, but she was glad she did. It was kind, thoughtful, and empathetic—not for Bonnie but for Tena, a person whom Karen barely knew, only that she was in charge.

Not that there was anything Tena or any of us could do but be by Patrick's side—stay and pray. We all knew what we had known since Amarillo: You can only live so long without platelets to defend against infection or internal bleeding, and Patrick had no platelets. Even sedated, he was still declining. Every day, another issue: low blood pressure, low-grade temperature, concerns about infection, coughing, low oxygen saturation, bleeding in his stomach that required a tube to drain . . . it didn't matter how great the hospital or doctors were. Whether they had the latest technology. Whether they were the most attentive clinicians in the world. Whether they gave him transfusions by the gallon. It was a horrible, sad, frustrating, worrisome, anxious time for all of us. Every day we hoped against hope to walk in and find his platelets had gone up and they would wake him up. Every day we learned a little more about how gruesome ITP can be. One day, Pat started bleeding into his eyes, which meant that when he woke up, he likely would be blind. Yet we kept saying *when,* not *if. When* they turn Pat's immune system around, are there going to be other complications that we needed to think about? What did we need to prepare for? Tena was a realist. She didn't want to get caught up in "he's going to get better and everything's going to go back to the way it was." Our Patrick was still alive but would be disabled. She and Bonnie started making a plan for living with those disabilities while caring for a baby. Which, for a brief shining moment nearly a month after Pat arrived in Seattle, seemed to be soon.

A lab report revealed the antibodies in Pat's blood that were destroying his platelets were dropping. He had been getting plasma pheresis, the removal and exchange of blood plasma, and there seemed to be results in platelet production—they appeared to be coming back. "We are seeing a light here," his doctor said. He was "cautiously optimistic." Knowing we hadn't been home in more than two months, Tena told us to go home and do our laundry, get stuff we needed, check in with Mark's dad and the dogs, and come back in a couple of days. We agreed and flew back to Sonoma. We made it home by midnight, hugged Mark's father and the dogs, and crashed.

At 3:00 A.M., the phone rang. It was Tena. "You had better come back," she said. The moist blood in Pat's lungs had created a problem. If it was an infection, they could treat it. If it was a mold, there was nothing they could do to stop it. He would die. By the time we made it back to Fred Hutch, they knew. It was a mold.

We had hours until the end. Family and friends said their goodbyes first. Then Tena. And Riley. As the door shut behind them, we stood on either side of Patrick and held his hands. A nurse whose name we don't know, but whose face and touch we will never forget, held our hands in hers. Another nurse came in to turn off the ventilator. It didn't take long.

On the early afternoon of November 6, 1999, eight weeks from the time he was first admitted into the hospital in Amarillo, J. Patrick Barnes passed away in Seattle.

Only then did we leave him alone.

The days after were filled with feelings of loss and love—and occasional laughter. While planning the celebration of his life at the country club he used to go to as a kid, we went with Tena to a funeral home that gave a 50 percent discount to anyone who died at Fred Hutch. Pat was going to be cremated but he apparently still needed to be in a box. We walked through the displays with names like Eternal Slumber and Whispering Pines with price tags of $25,000, $50,000, and more. Then we found it: The Cardboard, $200. We all had the same reaction: Pat would love it. He always loved a deal.

After the celebration, we headed back to Amarillo with Dianne to get Tena, Riley, and Griffey settled and to plan another celebration of Patrick's life for their friends and colleagues there. Our thoughts also turned to keeping Patrick's spirit alive after the celebrations of a life taken too soon were over. Pat had been gone for a week and left a gaping hole in our world we felt compelled to fill. And so the emptiness that consumed us was joined by a question—a question countless people ask in some way every day. A question that for us would define the work we would do for the rest of our lives.

Now what do we do?

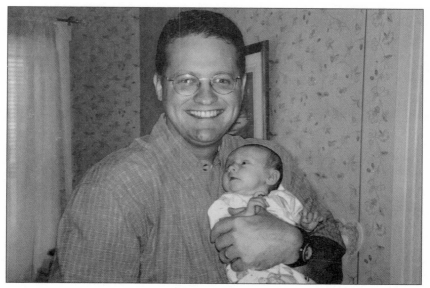

J. Patrick Barnes and his daughter, Riley, August 1999

Now What Do We Do?
1999–2008

"The DAISY Foundation allows me to live out my mission of inspiring nurses to be the best they can be by putting a spotlight on excellent nursing care and having a platform for nurses to see what a great nurse looks like."

Jennifer Magill, BSN, RN

Liquid Dinner

A father should get to know his newborn daughter. That baby girl should get to grow up with her devoted dad. A couple that has found true love should get to grow old together. Parents shouldn't lose a child—ever. That's not the way the world is supposed to work. But it happens. People leave us too soon. More than they ever should. More than anyone can or could prevent or understand. We lost Our Patrick: our son, husband, and father. When going through a loss this deep, it's only natural to feel the need to do something—*anything*—to fill the void.

On our second night in Amarillo, with the loss still raw and deep, we decided to fill that void with a liquid dinner: a lot of wine and a lot of tears. We headed to Outback Steakhouse with Tena and Dianne. And with Riley swinging in her baby swing on the side of the table, we came back to the question: *Now what do we do?* What were we going to do in Patrick's memory?

As the wine and tears flowed, we came up with three ideas. The first idea was the most obvious for a family struck down by a disease that they had no hope of understanding and could not be stopped: prevent what happened to Patrick from happening to someone else, so no patient and family would ever go through what we went through. We would start a nonprofit in Patrick's memory. We would fund research to cure ITP. We would call it The Foundation for the Elimination of Diseases Attacking the Immune System. Tena thought about the name. *Too long*, she thought, turning it over in her head. She then suggested shortening it and creating an acronym: **D**iseases **A**ttacking the **I**mmune **SY**stem or DAISY. The DAISY Foundation—in Memory of J. Patrick Barnes. Perfect.

The second idea originated with Bonnie: provide support for patients going through what Patrick went through who had no family to be by their side every day. She remembered how we were often the only family at the Fred Hutch bone marrow unit. There were patients in rooms up and down the halls, but they were usually alone. This was long before the days of sitters and Skype, and it had upset her and Mark. She wanted to find a way for people to not be alone in a place like Fred Hutch, where patients come from all over the world for treatment and don't have people to do what we did. Our foundation would coordinate volunteers to be with people when they were sick, to provide emotional support. So that, extending Patrick's final words to them, they did not have to be alone.

Up until this point, our liquid dinner ideas had been entirely too sad. We had a collective desire to focus on something positive, on something good because so much bad had happened. Besides, Pat was such a positive person. He would hate if everything a foundation set up in his memory did focused on what was wrong and did not celebrate all the right. As we thought about this, we kept coming back to our nurses. We fixated on them. We all talked about how we expected the clinical excellence, particularly at Fred Hutch, but we did not expect the way it was delivered and how the nurses made us feel. We remembered how important it was to the nurses caring for Patrick that they get to know him, even the ones he never spent a conscious minute with. They treated Pat like a whole person—who he was before he got sick and the man he would be once again when he was well. Tena said she would never forget how kind, gentle, loving, and tender they were, yet always professional and informative. They were her lifelines. They were her family before we returned to Amarillo from Italy.

We recalled stories of our nurses from the last two months. Dan and his sports trivia. The welcome delivery of Cinnabons that seemingly made us VIPs. The spaghetti dinner on their fifth anniversary. Tana making sure Mark did not faint on the floor when Pat involuntarily extubated his ventilator and blood flew around the room. Karen making sure Bonnie did not go home looking like Pat had died. The picture of Pat taped to his door. Every time nurses touched Patrick with loving hands. Every time they took the time to speak with us as we sat by his bedside in the middle of the night. Every hug.

The only sad part of our nurse conversation was realizing there are far too many Patricks in the world. As unique as it might feel to us and to every other person out there who is losing someone, especially someone too young to die, our situation was not unique. Nurses have seen just about everything, from the routine to the unimaginable. But *we* felt unique, and our nurses treated us this way. Maybe they had seen it all and saw everything as part of their job, but for families like ours and patients like Patrick, they saw us as individual human beings in their care. We then realized nurses are not always doing this in the service of making a bad or sad situation more bearable. Many times, it's a joyful time: helping a family welcome a child, making pain go away, treating someone sick and watching them get better. Every day, millions of nurses do one little thing to make patients feel like our nurses made us feel: that the patients are more than just charts and numbers in the system. That the patients are human beings, and so are the people who love them.

Our nurses comforted us and gave us the comfort level to feel it was okay to go get a cup of coffee, take a shower, get some sleep. They made our last days with Patrick more bearable. Less horrible. More human. They were, like Tena said, an extension of our family, and lifelines to the doctors and information we needed. We couldn't have trusted them more. After all, we trusted them with Patrick's life. How many people felt just the way we did and wished there was a way to thank them? How many nurses don't even see how what they do is so extraordinary, who just see it all as doing their job? They are unsung heroes to so many.

The more we talked, the more we truly felt Patrick's spirit guiding us at the table, reminding us how the nurses took care of him, leading us further into this idea: doing something to thank our nurses who had been so great to us and are so great to others around the country. And thanks to Tena we even had a name for it all: the DAISY Award—like the flower, reflecting the beauty and joy we wanted our work to embody, its roots in our mission of gratitude and Patrick's story. The DAISY Award would be a recognition program for nurses to honor and celebrate them all year long, sharing their stories of extraordinary compassionate care. We would start by sharing our story and honoring nurses at the two hospitals that took care of Pat and then grow from there. We would make sure the award wasn't a competition and that it was more than just an appreciation program or employee-of-the-month kind of thing. We wanted the DAISY Award to be something nurses were nominated for by other nurses—something that came from the heart and recognized moments of compassionate care like our nurses had given us. Our premise was: Who knows nurses better than other nurses? Knowing how busy nurses and hospitals often are, we resolved to make the whole process and ceremony turnkey; we would provide everything they needed to get going and to implement the program on an ongoing basis, so they could easily honor nurses all year long. We would also make it flexible so the hospitals could customize the program to fit their needs and cultures.

We could feel the energy of Pat's memory running through us as we moved on to what we might give the nurses who received the recognition. A certificate. A pin, of course—nurses love pins. Did you see all those pins they wore? Bonnie thought that since they work so hard and never think of themselves, we should give them a dinner for two at a nice restaurant and a massage so they could get back some of the physical comfort that they gave to their patients. We resolved to open a bank account as soon as we got back to California and start funding all three DAISY ideas ourselves while we applied for nonprofit status from the IRS. We would help cure ITP, support families, and recognize nurses. We would execute all of them immediately. Or so we thought.

DAISY HONOREE STORY[*]

Rebecca Schmit, BSN, RN
Children's Hospital Colorado
Aurora, Colorado

Becca has done so much with our Palliative Care Team in the NICU. I worked on day shift caring for one of my primary patients who was on palliative care while Becca was caring for him on night shift. She suggested the idea of a "bucket list" for our patient and his siblings, parents, and extended family members to check off while he was with us.

The family came up with ideas and Becca was the ringleader in getting the items on the list checked off. She was so creative with her ideas on how to pull off some of the activities! One of the things on the list was to have a day at the beach. Becca brought in play sand, a blow-up kiddie pool, a beach ball, sand toys, and even managed to borrow a heat lamp from the OR to make the "sunshine!" The family was elated and his siblings so enjoyed playing with him while he dipped his feet in the sand and water while wearing his swim trunks basking in the "sun" on night shift.

Becca arranged to have a Disco Dance Party, which was also on the bucket list. She brought in a plastic ball and some rhinestones so that his sisters could decorate the disco ball and get in on the fun as well. Another item on the list was to have a Nerd Day, and Becca made a onesie painted to look like it was a button-up oxford shirt with a pocket protector and some pencils inside. She found baby-size black glasses and put tape around the bridge of the nose. The pictures were so adorable!

The family would always be in such high spirits when Becca was around. She helped so much more than she realized! Not only did she inspire the patient's family, but she also inspired those of us who are privileged to work with her. She showed me that with just the right amount of heart and creativity, anything you can dream up is possible to do, even while in a Neonatal Intensive Care Unit!

I think it is very clear that Becca is a true DAISY Nurse. She would never expect such recognition for what she sees as just a part of her everyday life on the job.

---

* The DAISY Honoree stories in this book are reprinted (with permission) as submitted by the nominator, edited for privacy and small grammatical changes only to preserve the original nomination.

"We don't do this work for the recognition or thanks, but it was such an amazing feeling to receive the DAISY Award! It's so gratifying to be appreciated by those you care for and the team that helps you every day."

Angela Bacon, BSN, RN, CCRN

Picking the First DAISY

In the fairy tale movie about the making of the DAISY Foundation, we meet the doctors who can cure ITP soon after our liquid dinner and present them with all the money they need to make it happen. No one ever suffers from an immune disorder alone in a hospital. The DAISY Award rolls out with ease in Patrick's two hospitals, followed in hospitals across the nation clamoring to recognize and thank the unsung nurse heroes. Also, in that movie, Mark is played by British actor Idris Elba, and Bonnie plays herself. But reality is often a lot more work and not quite as pretty.

Things started well enough. We returned to Sonoma after Pat's memorials and funded a DAISY bank account. We filed the paperwork for 501(c)(3) nonprofit status with the IRS (which would be granted the following spring). A few business associates of Mark's made significant donations in Pat's memory and smaller amounts came in from family, friends, and others. By the end of 1999, we had about $50,000 in contributions in addition to our own, plenty to start our DAISY work.

Of course we also had our own work. Mark was back running his business in San Francisco. Bonnie was back running the vineyard and serving on the board of the grape growers association, doing their marketing and strategic planning. And Tena and Riley were with us. We had become very close to Tena during Pat's final journey. We had Thanksgiving in Amarillo, and then Tena returned to Sonoma with us. She had been building an advertising career in Atlanta and Memphis, but in Amarillo she had been an administrative assistant. There was no career for her to build there, no support network, and without Pat, no reason to stay. She needed to get back into advertising and make enough money to support herself and Riley. As much as we wanted them to stay in Sonoma and let us help with Riley, the cost of living was so high in California we couldn't afford to buy her a house, and the commute to San Francisco was so far she would never have time with Riley. It wasn't going to work. Instead, Tena's parents, who had moved away from Atlanta, said if she moved back there they would move back too, and help take care of the baby when she went to work. We promised to visit regularly.

So it was down to us and Dianne, who was back in Seattle, to move on with DAISY. DAISY just didn't want to get moving that quickly.

Our first idea that we could fund research to cure ITP started out well: We supported the work of Dr. George in Oklahoma City, who had consulted with Pat's doctors in Amarillo and recommended the bone marrow transplant. He and his students were researching treatment protocols for ITP. In a related idea, we decided to support the treatment of ITP by encouraging people to register as bone marrow donors and to help run blood drives. (The first one being held in Amarillo with the help of Pat's former employer and friends.) But the following year our idea that we could fund research to cure ITP faded as quickly as you could say $200,000. That's what the doctor who took us out for a nice dinner told us. We ended up giving him $25,000 to partially pay for a data analyst, and regretted it almost instantly. Another doctor who had developed one of the drugs that was tried on Patrick but did not work met with us and said it would cost $100,000 just to open a door to a research facility. We backed out of his door politely instead of making the same mistake.

Our second idea that we could create a national support network for patients alone in hospitals fizzled after we sobered up and thought things through. We realized it was probably impractical to develop and tend to a network of volunteers. We didn't know enough people to even lay the groundwork at the hospitals we knew, and there was no control over when people would be needed. But while we abandoned our idea for creating a support network on our own, we planned to help the ITP Support Association in the United Kingdom and the Platelet Disorder Support Association in the United States, both of which served patients with diseases like the one Patrick had. We hoped they could establish a network of compassionate and caring people to reach out to families affected by immune system disease.

Our first two ideas from the liquid dinner might have been on a bumpy path, but we did present them upfront in our first official announcement of the DAISY Foundation "dedicated to Pat's memory, positive spirit, and sense of humor." The nurse recognition program that would define DAISY for the next two decades was in the announcement, too. We talked about how fortunate we were to have had the support of such competent and compassionate doctors and nurses. How touched we were by their dedication and grace. How the nurses in particular were our unsung heroes. How we were thus establishing a recognition program for nurses who provide extraordinary compassionate care featuring a personalized thank-you, dinner at a wonderful restaurant, and a spa treatment. And if that sounds exactly like where we were months before, then give yourself a DAISY pin. Actually, the DAISY pin was one of the few parts of the DAISY Award we were able to move forward on. We created it and the DAISY Award certificate. We just had no one to give them to . . . yet.

We started out hopeful. We decided to take our idea for the DAISY Award program to Fred Hutchinson Cancer Research Center in Seattle first. We flew back to Seattle to present it and got a positive reaction from the managers of Patrick's unit but also some news: Implementing it immediately would be impossible. Fred Hutch, which had been renting inpatient space at Swedish Hospital, had joined with the University of Washington Medical Center and Seattle Children's to create the Seattle Cancer Care Alliance. The new alliance would be housed at the university and planned to open its first inpatient unit in 2000. If we wanted to wait a year or so, they would be happy to revisit our idea.

We decided to wait. We felt we couldn't go to the other hospitals until we knew it worked in the place that last took care of Patrick—the one that shared our story. While we waited, we revisited our idea. We still had confidence in it. We even enhanced it, adding the delivery of Cinnabons for all the nurses on the unit, just like Pat had asked us to do in Amarillo—just like he would have done himself if he had survived. But then we started thinking: Those rolls had gone over big time with his nurses, but would DAISY? We knew from our research there was no national nursing recognition program for compassionate care. But maybe there was a reason for that. How were the nurses going to respond? Was this going to cause conflict? Even if it wasn't a competition and was given on a regular basis, would it be perceived as a competition? We come from advertising. We have been through award seasons and heard the polite applause when people win and then heard the chatter that they didn't deserve it. We didn't think nurses would be like that, but what did we know? The Cinnabons would make sure that they celebrated together but could they prevent conflict and jealousy? Would they eat them and still walk away mad? *Would DAISY's desire to shine a light on the positive be seen as a negative?* We would have our answer soon enough.

We also wondered if any of Patrick's nurses remained at Fred Hutchinson. Without them to honor, we didn't think anyone there would connect to Pat's and our story and DAISY as deeply. We were wrong. Turned out, two people at the UW Medical Center felt that connection: Cindy Angiulo and Susan Grant. Two people who would mean more to the foundation's future than we ever could have imagined when we met them and learned our first DAISY lesson in the power of great relationships.

There's an old saying that there are always three sides to every story: yours, mine, and the truth. In thousands of presentations about DAISY's origin, we have told the story of how from the start we wanted the nurses' recognition to be based on a nomination from their colleagues for their compassionate care, not clinical excellence. No manager or administrators playing favorites or playing office politics. No names picked at random from a hat. Yet picked from a hat is exactly how the Seattle Cancer Care Alliance at UW Medical Center decided to proceed with their first DAISY Award in February 2001.

Our story has always been that it really upset us, and it did, because a few of Patrick's nurses did remain at Fred Hutch and could have been honored through a nomination by a fellow nurse. What we have never shared is that we knew the recipient would be chosen at random. We supported that approach at first, because if we hadn't, we knew DAISY might never have been awarded at all.

It was a letter from Dianne on DAISY's behalf dated November 20, 2000, written following her conversation with a university hospital administrator we have no recollection of meeting, that revealed this truth to us. Most of it covered the basics about rewarding one nurse per month with a dinner and spa treatment and presenting the award and pin along with a delivery of Cinnabons to the staff. It talked about Pat and our desire to keep the program as simple as possible, as well as flexible: "their opinions and desires would determine our next course of action." And then there was this: "Here's how the program might work. You determine the recipient of the month randomly as we discussed."

Shining the Light on All the Right

It was nearly two decades after Dianne wrote this letter that we found it in an old file and read it again. Both of us wondered *Why would we have agreed to that*? Not Dianne, *us*. We spoke with one voice when it came to DAISY. There was also a line about keeping the value of the dinner and treatment under a certain dollar amount. Why? Because Dianne knew much more than her letter stated. She knew what the university wanted and needed in order for Cindy Angiulo to launch the program—and we would be forever grateful for that. Because Cindy was our first guardian angel.

When we had met Cindy earlier in the year, she captured our hearts as much as she says we captured hers. Cindy was the assistant administrator nurse at UW Medical Center at the time and had made it her charge to put the DAISY program together there to support her work with the Seattle Cancer Care Alliance. Just before Pat passed away, Cindy had been tasked with building a new nursing culture at the university around the Alliance. She not only had to bring the nurses from the other organizations together as university employees but also had to recruit new nurses and get them all working together for something different from what she or any nurse had experienced. On top of that, everybody including the university's nurses had to rebid for their positions, from the top down. "It was a very stressful time," Cindy recalls. "Nobody knew what the new environment would be like. Even after the first ten beds opened it was a shaky time culturally for everything there. People were used to what they were used to."

DAISY, Cindy thought, was something different, too. She felt integrating DAISY would fit into what she was trying to accomplish. She had decided to implement it regularly into the weekly offsite education day for all the nurses. "It was very special. It added to the good feelings nurses had in having a day devoted to them. It was something everyone could agree on and support. My whole goal was integrating nurses from three different organizations. DAISY could unify everyone. There was nothing better that we could do. But we had to be thoughtful as to the politics of it." That's because DAISY wasn't for all the nurses in the medical center, only for the Seattle Cancer Care Alliance, and that created some controversy. The Fred Hutch unit was a showcase for the university, but she had to be careful that didn't scream their nurses were better than any others at the university's medical center. And it being a state institution, Cindy had to be cautious about what they gave as gifts. Hence the dollar limit.

Then there was controversy around selecting the recipients, which explained the rest of Dianne's letter. Cindy hated the idea of the random drawing as much as we did. She wanted specific criteria for nominations or at least to get nurses' nominations together and then put *them* in the theoretical hat, not *every* nurse's name. But she had not been involved in those discussions. The university saw the idea of the drawing as inclusive, nonthreatening, and easier. Cindy didn't agree with the first point, but she saw the value in the other two. "It was a very tenuous time," she recalls. "Folks were threatened by much more than just DAISY in this new environment, and leadership didn't want anyone to feel more threatened. They wanted DAISY implemented, but they wanted to avoid any dissent. A drawing meant they didn't have to agree on anything. They just had to pick a name."

In the end, they picked two—Kenna Smith Shangrove and Carolyn Stormer—and we travelled to Seattle in February 2001 to present with Dianne the DAISY Award for the first time. We brought the award certificates, the frames for which Mark had spared no expense at Costco. We brought the pins. We brought the Cinnabons. We brought more family who wanted to share in a day that honored Patrick. As we walked from the car into the building, we felt great anticipation: What would we experience? What would the nurses be like? *What would we say?*

It seems silly to us now—given that DAISY today has a sample script with very specific instructions on what presenters are to say and how to make it truly mean something to the nurses—that we would have prepared nothing. But that story is the truth. We didn't know what DAISY would become, and the first recipients were not chosen as we imagined. So we winged it. We talked about what a great experience we had being with them, that they were kicking us off, what DAISY meant to us, a bit about Patrick and his care, and how we just wanted to say thank you. We presented them with the pin and certificate, which they loved, and gift certificates for dinner for two and a massage that

Bonnie had arranged at two local places. The university honored the nurses they had chosen and said they would carry on with the program. We urged them to do it every month and make it an experience the honorees would remember for the rest of their lives.

What we were also unprepared for was how fast these nurses dashed any of our fears that there would be tension or unintended negative consequences as a result of getting a DAISY Award. Kenna and Carolyn were terrific. The other nurses all said things like "You couldn't have picked better nurses" and "This is great." We could only think how great it would feel if the nurses themselves nominated the recipients, which is exactly what Cindy Angiulo arranged to do next.

As the Alliance's unit got bigger and the team evolved together, their reputation at the university soared. That changed everything, so Cindy moved to make the changes she and we wanted: coming up with objective criteria for the nominating process and allowing nurses to do the nominating. She saw in DAISY the possibilities for creating more

Presenting the first DAISY Award to Kenna Smith Shangrove at the University of Washington Medical Center, Seattle, February 2001

than a great culture: She also pushed to expand it beyond the one unit to all three floors of the new Alliance and even to ambulatory care. She knew that stories of great nurses were everywhere: "I love stories that celebrate inspiring others to be the best they can be and recognize people. It's always been about the stories. DAISY captured the intimacy of the care *all* nurses provide. We're given a gift to be in the lives of patients and families and there's no more intimate time ever."

There was just one problem: They didn't get any nominations from nurses. That's when we learned another important lesson about nurses that is true to this day: They don't see themselves as heroes. It's just who they are and what they do. If we had a nickel for the number of times nurses who received a DAISY said, "I'm just doing my job. I'm not doing anything special," we'd have thousands of dollars more to spend on DAISY. So after two months, we asked if the university would open it up to patients. Bonnie made up patient nomination forms and marketing materials to show them how it could work. Cindy loved the idea. But to do that she needed help advocating for the change. She needed the buy-in of the university's chief nursing officer, Susan Grant, who couldn't have been more on board.

We had met Susan in March 2000, not long after she started at UW Medical Center. She came from the Dana Farber Cancer Institute in Boston where she had spent significant time implementing programs that involved patients and families. She was moved by the idea of DAISY being that kind of program.

"When I met Bonnie and Mark, I was overwhelmed," she remembers. "Here was a family whose son had passed away and they wanted to recognize nurses and the impact that the nurses had on his care. They were representing not only their own voices but wanted to represent the voices of other patients and families. Really recognizing nurses and being able to define and highlight what outstanding and excellent nursing care looked like from the patient and family standpoint. For nurses, there's nothing more meaningful than to be recognized by patients and/ or their families and to know that you've done something that made a difference for them. I knew in my core this was profoundly valuable."

Susan also knew there was no better place to pioneer this than the University of Washington. After all, it was the first hospital ever to receive Magnet designation through the Magnet Recognition Program® of the American Nurses Credentialing Center, demonstrating its excellence in nursing and patient outcomes. Being a Magnet hospital meant the university excelled in recruitment and retention of registered nurses. It was a place where nursing and professional practice were already valued. DAISY was a natural fit.

In addition, Susan didn't think DAISY would or should stop at the Alliance or the university, either. She believed there wasn't a chief nursing officer in the country who wouldn't want the DAISY program in their organization. It would give family members and patients an avenue to express how great their nurses were and how compassionate their care had been. She vowed to help make that happen.

And she did—and she was mostly right about all of what she thought. But as we said, reality isn't as pretty and takes much more time. Time that tested our resilience.

DAISY HONOREE STORY

Intensive Care Unit Team
Southern New Hampshire Medical Center ICU
Nashua, New Hampshire

There was a patient being cared for in the ICU for a month with end-stage pulmonary issues. He initially made progress but then began a steady decline and was unable to tolerate minimal life activities without intense shortness of breath. The ICU team spent a lot of time with the patient and family helping them choose a plan of care. The patient chose to not be resuscitated and ultimately wanted to remove his oxygen all together and be made comfortable. The ICU staff developed a significant bond with this patient and family and admired their strength and courage. The patient wanted to spend one last weekend with his family on his own terms. The ICU and Respiratory staff made every effort to compassionately honor his end of life requests.

While the ICU team was waiting for this patient's family to arrive from out of state, they had time to talk with him about his life and his family. It was clear how much he adored his family, and he mentioned that he had some young grandchildren. One nurse was trying to think of ways to make the experience less upsetting for his family when they arrived, so she asked more about them. The patient told her that he had a tradition of eating Oreos with his grandkids every time they visited at home, but instead of just giving them the Oreos, he would hide packages of them all around the house like an Easter egg hunt. His tradition with his own children was that they would drink a little scotch together every now and then. He and his wife also owned horses.

The nurse made a trip to the retail pharmacy across the street from the hospital and bought a bunch of Oreos, mugs for the scotch, and two little unicorns for him to give to his wife as a last present, because she couldn't find horses. She hid the Oreos all around the room while he was sleeping so that he would be surprised when he woke up. The respiratory therapist went to pediatrics to scout out decorating supplies, and she and the rest of the nurses helped to cut out paper hearts to decorate the room while the patient was sleeping.

When he woke up, he was so excited that there was a surprise that he could share with each member of his family. The nurse, leading this effort, was able to watch the grandchildren do the Oreo hunt in the patient's room. Pediatrics also gave the ICU a light-up wand, which the patient thought was just the best thing. He had so much fun showing it to his grandkids. When the family first arrived, everyone looked so anxious. The nurse escorted the family into the room to an experience that was fun instead of scary, and the grandchildren got to do something that was familiar to them. These activities provided a great deal of comfort for his wife.

"This little pin can mean so much. It keeps nurses going. Pushing, fighting, striving to be better. To do more. Recognition from the people we care for is the steam in our engines."

Megan Mowatt, BSN, RN

Getting It

Bonnie: "We had a fight."

Mark: "It wasn't a fight."

Bonnie: "It felt like a fight to me."

Mark: "It was an aggressive discussion with loud voices."

Bonnie: ". . ."

❀ ❀ ❀

Shining the Light on All the Right

We're remembering an afternoon in July 2004, more than three years after we presented our first awards at the University of Washington Medical Center. Twenty hospitals had signed up for the DAISY Awards. We had celebrated hundreds of nurses. But adding those hospitals, sustaining them, and making sure the nurses availed themselves of the spa treatment and dinner was proving difficult and time consuming. An entrepreneur by trade and at heart, Mark saw the hours Bonnie was putting into DAISY—the cold calling, the hurry-up-and-wait, the follow-up—and he was frustrated. Not unhappy, frustrated.

"What the heck are we doing here?" Mark aggressively wondered. "Every hospital is just as hard as the last one. You're working very hard for very little. The amount of time spent calling and calling. The constant questioning. All to give this to people and places who don't seem to want it. Something's not clicking. Maybe we should just focus on sustaining what we have."

Bonnie understood where Mark was coming from. They were both proud of how far DAISY had come but its growth was not proportional to Bonnie's effort. Results seemed to be flagging: We were on pace to add fewer hospitals than the year before. "I was making cold calls and people were turning us down. It was free, patient- and family-generated, turnkey. Still, I would hear, 'Is this for real?' They were skeptical 'You want to do what? At no cost?' Many more of those responses than 'How do we start!?'" Bonnie also heard a refrain that would follow DAISY for the first years of its journey: Nurses didn't need recognition for the things they do every day.

Yet Bonnie remained optimistic—not "cautiously optimistic," words she and Mark swore never to use again after hearing them from the doctor the day before Patrick died, but fully optimistic. Hence, the fight . . . um, aggressive discussion. After all, DAISY had come so far—which was exactly why Bonnie didn't share Mark's frustration. The DAISY Awards *were* growing, more than we had expected when we presented our first awards in 2001. The University of Washington *Daily* covered that event, and Bonnie told them we hoped we would get to say thank you to nurses in ten hospitals around the country. We had doubled that. Twenty hospitals might be less than one-half of 1 percent of all the hospitals in the United States, but it was an accomplishment, especially for something that had never been done before, led by people who weren't from the healthcare industry. Things were happening. DAISY had donors and sponsors. We had attended presentations at every new hospital and seen what it meant to the nurses. Some of those hospitals had had no connection to us in the beginning, which had not been the case when we launched DAISY.

Actually, the first DAISY hospitals had come fairly quickly after UW Medical Center and Baptist Saint Anthony in Amarillo, where Pat's final journey began, and they came largely from relationships we or the people we knew had with those hospitals. Cedars-Sinai Medical Center in Los Angeles was the third to join and came through Lynne Doll, a dear friend of ours from the advertising world who later joined our board (and whom we sadly lost to cancer in 2010 at the age of 48). After her father died at Cedars-Sinai, Lynne told Bonnie he had received great care, and Bonnie asked if he had any great nurses. "We had incredible nurses," Lynne replied. Bonnie suggested we bring DAISY to the hospital, and Lynne and her family loved the idea of honoring her dad's nurses with the DAISY program. Lynne offered to sponsor it as a tribute to her father. Lynne's doctor was a world leader in brain surgery, and when his nurse became the hospital's first honoree, he came over to us and thanked us after the presentation. "This is really special," he said.

Sonoma Valley Hospital, where Mark's father passed, came soon after Cedars-Sinai. His homecare nurse, Steve Turme, received their first award. We added a hospital in Reno when the daughter-in-law of close friends of ours, Judy and Bruce England, gave birth to twins very prematurely. When one of the babies died, the England family helped us bring DAISY to Washoe Medical Center (which became Renown Health). Santa Rosa Memorial Hospital started after good friends got into a car accident and were treated there. All in all, we had seven hospitals presenting DAISY Awards by the end of 2002, including the first from a cold call: NewYork-Presbyterian Weill Cornell Medical Center in New York City.

Bonnie, a born and bred New Yorker, wanted to do something—*anything*—to support the city she loved after the 9/11 terrorist attacks and thought the DAISY Award would do some good. She chose NewYork-Presbyterian because of its world-renowned burn unit. She thought victims of the attack must have been taken there. She waited several weeks to reach out because she figured the hospital must be overwhelmed. When she felt it was appropriate to call, Bonnie realized she didn't know whom to call. She still didn't fully understand the structure of nursing. She tried the general volunteer line and nursing offices first and got no response. When Bonnie finally got someone to call her back and explained what DAISY wanted to do, the person knew exactly whom to put us in touch with: the director of nursing operations, Cynthia Godfrey. She listened to the DAISY story and why Bonnie had reached out to them in particular. She told Bonnie she was partially right: The burn unit had indeed been overwhelmed immediately following the attack with some of the most severely burned and badly injured patients they had ever seen. Every resource the hospital could spare shifted to the burn unit. The entire hospital had been prepared for the halls to be lined with beds, but had not received nearly as many victims as expected. Many escaped, but few still in the World Trade Center towers at the time of their collapse survived. But if Bonnie still wanted to bring DAISY to NewYork-Presbyterian in general, she said she would support it.

As we did for every hospital in our first years, we flew in to present the first award. Presenting in New York City was a tremendous experience—almost as tremendous as the sports jacket the first honoree had to wear. The nurse was a lovely Irish man, John Fiddler, who was big on compassion but small in stature. After a wonderful ceremony, Cynthia arranged for a lunch with the hospital's chief operating officer, Richard D'Aquila. He took us and the nurse to the Faculty Club (something he would do for future DAISY Honorees while he was in that position). Only problem: Jackets were required. As the award and the lunch were a surprise, John hadn't worn a jacket to work. The club had a spare on hand, but the size 48 swam on his much smaller frame.

While that nurse had no hope of filling out that jacket, DAISY was filling out quite nicely, it seemed, and we wanted to make sure everyone knew. We had started a newsletter in December 2000, announcing the launch of DAISY. It featured our first logo: a bunch of supermarket daisies we photographed in Dianne's kitchen in Seattle. The July 2001 newsletter announced our first three hospitals. In November 2002, the newsletter proudly listed the names of 76 DAISY recipients. Around this time, we also launched our first website. Looking back, we can't believe how rudimentary it all feels, yet wholly and genuinely reflective of DAISY at the time: homemade, grassroots, and of course fully honoring Patrick's memory.

In those early newsletters, we also announced proudly that we had received a grant from Johnson & Johnson, which was starting their campaign for nurses. Yes, it took us more than a day to fill out what felt like a 5,000-page application. But while it was a lot of work for the $1,000 we received, it was our first external affirmation of DAISY from a major company that had never met us, and it was a meaningful amount of money to us at the time. We received the same grant and a little more in the following two years but, then Johnson & Johnson dropped their grant program. As much work as it was for applicants to fill out an application, the company realized it was more work to read all of them!

We also announced our first corporate sponsor for a specific participating organization in our early newsletters: America West Airlines (which later became USAir), the company that helped us develop our entire approach to corporate sponsorship.

We met America West through one of our early partners, Hospice of the Valley in Phoenix. We had been introduced to the Hospice by a friend of Bonnie's mom. The Hospice was headed by Susan Goldwater Levine, the widow of the former senator and presidential candidate, Barry Goldwater. She is also a nurse—the kind of nurse who would jump out of a moving car to save someone. We know this because she almost did jump out of our moving car when we saw an accident. A motorcycle had been hit by a car. Susan tended to the motorcyclist, holding him, giving him a moment of comfort before he died. It was a very disturbing thing for us to experience—a man dying in Susan's arms like that—but it showed us who she was and is: a nurse through and through.

That evening, we attended the Hospice of the Valley fundraiser as her guests. We had a table and a DAISY sign prominently displayed, explaining DAISY's mission. America West was there, too. Their head of government affairs was impressed with what we were doing. He had lost his wife at the Hospice, and the nurses there had made a huge difference to him. We asked if he might like to sponsor the DAISY Award at the Hospice as a way of saying thank you to those nurses. He agreed, and that led to our connection to the airline sponsoring DAISY in hospitals in their most active destinations, such as Charlotte and Pittsburgh. Over the years, America West staff would join us at DAISY Award presentations—something we learned would be an important offer to future industry partners, such as Hill-Rom, a manufacturer of healthcare equipment. We were introduced to Melissa Fitzpatrick, then Hill-Rom's chief clinical officer, a nurse who loved what we were doing and saw the potential for a mutually beneficial relationship. We felt strongly from the start that we didn't want to depend on "checkbook charity." We wanted to partner with companies that shared our passion for nurses and with which we would develop unique marketing relationships. Hill-Rom became our model for that.

And then there was Cinnabon. Its cinnamon rolls were one of the happiest memories we had of Patrick during his final months, and we wanted them to be a part of every DAISY presentation. So we reached out. We started appropriately with the marketing director to ask the company to donate or at least sell us Cinnabons at cost. He refused our call. But unlike at NewYork-Presbyterian, we knew exactly where to go next—to the person who's really in charge of most companies: the boss's secretary. Within minutes of explaining DAISY, we got a call back from the same marketing director who earlier had refused our call. He agreed to pay for a box of Cinnabons for every box we bought. Soon after, a box full of thousands of $5 gift certificates arrived in the mail. When those ran out, Cinnabon sent more. We sent the hospitals personal checks to cover the other half.

Years later, Cinnabon got a new president, Geoff Hill, and public relations director, Jennifer Dempsey. Jennifer saw the meaning in what we were doing for nurses, and how DAISY might benefit the Cinnabon brand. So she invited us to come to Atlanta to meet Geoff. Over dinner, after hearing us describe DAISY and how we had integrated Cinnabon into every DAISY Award presentation, he said, "We're not doing nearly enough for you. What more can we do?" Mark told him that we were writing personal checks to hospitals to pay for half the Cinnabons they bought. Geoff said, "Well, that's going to stop. We'll pay for them all." But as each bakery was a franchise, Geoff asked that we make a presentation to his Franchise Advisory Council to get final approval. The presentation went great, and we asked Jennifer to join our board. As DAISY grew, we added hospitals in areas where Cinnabon didn't have bakeries. Jennifer's solution was to provide jars of its signature Makara cinnamon. We called it "DAISY Dust." Just like the cinnamon rolls, it served as a sweet reminder to nurses that they make a difference in patients' lives. Cinnabon continued to donate rolls nationally until we outgrew their franchise system and we had to discontinue the program in an official capacity, which wasn't easy for any of us. (Most hospitals accepted it, but there was one that threatened to discontinue the program without the free Cinnabons. They didn't.) To this day, however, the company supports DAISY with a National Nurses Week giveaway of Cinnabons to nurses and provides them at DAISY conference events. They have donated more than one million of their cinnamon rolls.

But perhaps no relationship in those nascent years meant more to DAISY's growth than Bonnie Lasky.

Bonnie Lasky is a long-time friend of ours, and by 2001 she had retired as the risk manager at the University of California at San Francisco and San Francisco General Hospital. The Bonnies had been close during the time Patrick was hospitalized. Knowing Bonnie Lasky's experience, over lunch one day Bonnie said, "Come and work with us on the DAISY program."

Bonnie Lasky jumped right in. She saw we only had a few hospitals and little way for others to find out about DAISY without hearing from us. So she got her stepdaughter, Rebecca, to help create that first website. After the website was up and running, Bonnie Lasky said, "Let's go to all the UC [University of California] hospitals." She had been the assistant director at UC Davis Medical Center in Sacramento before she went to San Francisco, and she introduced us to the chief nursing officer, Carol Robinson. DAISY did the work from there. "I know nurses are doing great things every day in this hospital," Carol told us. "DAISY will give us a way to capture their stories and celebrate them." Bonnie Lasky also opened the door at other hospitals that she knew, like Children's Hospital Oakland and the Alta Bates Hospital also in Oakland. But perhaps as much as the introductions, Bonnie gave us insight. She told us, "Every hospital has its own personality and way of doing business." For example, San Francisco General had to go through the city council, which had a lot of rules and regulations on what the hospital could do. Understanding that got us ready to deal with county and safety net hospitals—where nurses really deserved to be recognized but it would take some time to get through the system.

Bonnie Lasky's influence was our first big education in the power of relationships within the hospital world to open doors, and why we knew it would take a lot of patience, persistence, and resilience to get DAISY growing. It was bound to move slower than Mark the entrepreneur wanted. Our process of forming those relationships and developing them, and our learning from and listening to nurses, was just beginning. We were new. It was bound to be messy. We needed to help nurses and hospital administrators get it—to see why DAISY and its ongoing recognition of those nurses was important—and then we needed to be patient when things dragged a bit. Still, by mid 2003 we had five new DAISY hospitals thanks to Bonnie Lasky, and we asked her to be the first nonfamily member to join our board to help us through it all.

Shining the Light on All the Right

But even with all Bonnie Lasky's help, we couldn't open all the doors we needed and wanted to. Our momentum seemed to be slowing as we entered 2004. Which brings us back to our "aggressive discussion" that summer. Bonnie understood Mark's frustration with DAISY's growth and, despite her optimism, didn't want to torture him more than necessary. So she made a promise: "Just let me get to 50, and I'll quit. Let me get 50 hospitals, and I'll stop cold calling and just run what we have." Mark agreed, and Bonnie became more determined than ever to get those hospitals and honor those nurses with the recognition and the spa treatment and night out they deserved. Well, all except the spa treatment and night out. They went away in the following year because of one woman: Ann Dechairo-Marino, the chief nursing officer at one of our DAISY hospitals, Northridge Medical Center in Southern California.

Bonnie knew in her head that Mark was right about the amount of energy she was putting in to get the spas and restaurants lined up for nurses who mostly didn't take advantage of them. But Bonnie couldn't let it go. She feared taking these gifts away from nurses, especially those in hospitals where DAISY was already established, would make future honorees feel they were worth less than the ones who came before. It was Ann who changed her mind. We were at Northridge Medical Center for a presentation and Bonnie mentioned to Ann how we did all this work to set up the spa treatment and dinner and how few nurses took advantage of them. She asked Ann why she thought this was happening. Ann looked at Bonnie.

Bonnie and DAISY as a whole have never forgotten Ann's words: *Don't you get it? It's about the recognition.*

Such a profound lesson in just eight words—simple yet powerful. On a practical level, Ann changed the way we thought and worked. Apparently we hadn't gotten it—not completely—and DAISY wouldn't be anywhere near where we are today if Bonnie hadn't heard Ann—*really listened*—and instead continued to spend half her time trying to set up benefits for nurses that were not really meaningful or relevant to them. We stopped offering the spa treatment and dinner to new hospitals and phased it out at the existing ones. Not one hospital or nurse complained. Mark had been right.

Shining the Light on All the Right

On a more philosophical level, Ann's words affirmed what we did get: the importance of showing appreciation for people so they know the impact they have on us. Not only to nurses but to everyone in our lives. The importance of gratitude—of saying thank you for the little things that others do to make our lives better without any expectation of return. That was what we were honoring in Patrick's memory. That was the DAISY mission.

Fourteen years later, we ran into Ann at a nursing conference. We hadn't seen her in ages. Bonnie told Ann she probably didn't realize what an impact she had on DAISY. That her words supporting our dropping dinners and massages had freed up time for us to reach out to more hospitals, and made a big difference in the expansion of our work. Ann looked at us: "I had no idea I made that kind of difference." It felt to us what it must be like to write a DAISY nomination—a chance to tell someone the impact they had made when they didn't know it. And like a true nurse, she had no idea what a difference she made.

But while Ann may have been right that we didn't get it in one way, we did get it in another—in a way that wasn't even part of the original DAISY idea. Something that, unlike the dinner and spa treatment, nurses have treasured since we introduced it in our second year. Something the American Organization of Nurse Executives found so beautiful and significant that it was the only thing pictured as part of a front-page article on DAISY in its July 2004 newsletter. Something that became symbolic of the relationships nurses have with their patients. Something that delivered a message of recognition in a way no massage or meal ever could. The sculpture that has come to express the very meaning of the DAISY Awards: *The Healer's Touch.*

DAISY HONOREE STORY

Justin Williford, RN
Children's of Alabama
Birmingham, Alabama

My son Matthew has cerebral palsy and lung disease. He has been in several children's hospitals and his condition has worsened over the years, so that two years ago he had a tracheostomy and on April 15 he was placed on a ventilator he will be on the rest of his life. Justin began caring for Matthew on April 21. He is a 7-on/7-off employee and he had Matthew for his entire week. Matthew is nonverbal but communicates through his many varied facial expressions.

I have just recently discovered that Matthew loves sci-fi. He laughs and grins when he can watch a movie, but due to his vision impairment, he can't see the large screen on the wall in his room. I wanted to connect a DVD player to the smaller TV that is on a boom and move it closer to his face so that he could actually see the screen. Justin called maintenance one day while I was at work and made it happen. I walked into Matthew's room and there he was, grinning ear to ear, watching *Star Wars* and having a grand time.

Justin also plays Matthew's iPod in the morning and "jams" with him, as he calls it, while doing his morning assessment, mouth care and so forth. Matthew adores Justin too, and likes to play tricks on him. My other child is autistic and I often have to go home and spend time with him as well. So on Sunday while I was at home and Justin had Matthew, I called to see how the day was going. After the conversation I thanked Justin for taking such great care of Matthew.

His response brought tears to my eyes. He said, "No, thank you for having such an awesome son." To a mom who has seen her child ignored at best and spoken down to at worst, finding a nurse who sees the jewel that Matthew is and actually enjoys his company is a blessing, and instills such confidence in the care Justin gives.

We are so blessed to have Justin on the Children's team, and I should know because I too am a nurse employed here at Children's.

"Having received the DAISY Award reminds me that there are those people out there who understand. It makes the hard days easier. I see The Healer's Touch *on my dresser, and I know the day is going to be okay."*

Michele Robison, RN

The Healer's Touch

The nurse dropped her *Healer's Touch* sculpture. She was so excited she was shaking as we presented it to her along with her DAISY pin and certificate, and it just slipped through her hands. Excitement turned to shock as it cracked into pieces on the floor. She gasped, as did the auditorium applauding her—and if you're among the millions of DAISY Honorees and Nominees, chances are you also gasped. That's how important the *Healer's Touch* has become to the DAISY Awards and the nurses who receive them.

We did not gasp. Before her shock turned to tears, we told the nurse and the audience not to worry; we had another sculpture to replace it. Like each nurse-patient relationship, each *Healer's Touch* is a unique creation. But unlike those relationships, the sculptures are replaceable—a great relief to our honoree and the hundreds of nurses and their family members who have called and emailed over the years, devastated that something happened to their sculpture. Not as many get emotional and call about losing their pins or their certificates. The *Healer's Touch* goes deeper; it has a perpetual essence. We hear countless stories of nurses giving their sculptures places of honor in their homes. As several chief nursing officers told us, the *Healer's Touch* speaks to who they are as human beings—to their compassion and what patients receive from them every day. It's not hyperbole to say it has become a special symbol to nurses. More than 400 hospitals have ordered three-foot-tall versions of the sculptures to grace their healing gardens and lobbies. The *Healer's Touch* also has a spiritual connection to its source: More than 20 gifted artists and their teams in Zimbabwe create them for DAISY all year long to support their entire extended families.

This lasting significance of the *Healer's Touch* sculptures amazes us considering they were not part of the original DAISY idea.

In 2002 we knew we wanted to add a permanent gift to the award beyond the pin, certificate, Cinnabons, the dinner and spa treatment— something uniquely DAISY. We didn't know what the gift should be, nor did we plan on it becoming *that* important. We just wanted something memorable to present. What we did know was that we did not want it to be some kind of trophy, no Oscar-like statuette. While some call DAISY the Oscar of nursing, we have never referred to our DAISY Honorees as winners. The DAISY Award is not about winning; it's about gratitude. We wanted a gift of gratitude.

We didn't have to go far to find the right one. Walking through a local gallery, we spotted a sculpture called *Mother and Child*. Carved in

Zimbabwe of serpentine stone, it was a classic design of the country's Shona artists, masters of stone cutting for thousands of years. Both of us remembered it from our travels in southern Africa and felt it perfectly captured and symbolized the nurse-patient relationship: One figure taller than the other but the two inseparable, their arms blending and holding each other up, equal pillars of support. It became even more meaningful when we learned of the profound respect and deep affection the Shona people have for their healers. They are called "treasures" by those they care for, and their well-being and safety is of community-wide importance. This described exactly how everyone

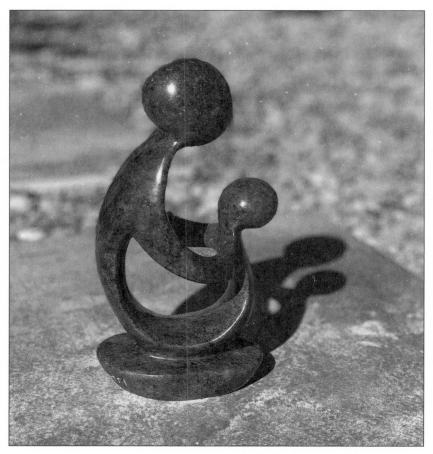

The Healer's Touch made by Shona artists of Zimbabwe

who touches DAISY feels about nurses! We decided to rechristen the mother-child sculptures we would present as *The Healer's Touch* to honor this connection between these worlds. We placed an order with a local gallery and expected to receive them the following year.

Why so long? We needed dozens of them, and the process of carving these stunning sculptures into works of art takes Shona artists almost two weeks to complete. Chisels, mallets, and chasing hammers shape the raw stone into the sculpture's form, proportion, and size. Raspers, water, and waterpapers (a kind of sandpaper) leave it round and smooth for heating and polishing. The entire process takes about two weeks to complete before the artists sign them.

When our first signed *Healer's Touch* sculptures finally arrived in 2003, the gallery packaged them handsomely in black boxes, and we headed to Sonoma Valley Hospital to present one for the first time. The response was like nothing we had seen at a presentation before but would repeat for years to come. We knew we had something special—a piece of art nurses and DAISY could call their own that they also saw as a symbol of the care they provide. As we prepared to ship sculptures to all the hospitals with their awards, we figured we had all systems in place for the foreseeable future. The massage and meal were being phased out. The *Healer's Touch* would become the only gift to go with the pin, certificate, and, of course, the Cinnabons. We had a process in place to get as many as we needed. Like so many times in our journey, we were wrong. After a few years, the production of the *Healer's Touches* created as much anxiety in us as it did joy in the nurses. As DAISY grew, supply was inconsistent, often late, and the production lacked standardization: Every sculpture was a different size and shape. We needed more than we could get, and we needed a better price. We were not sure what to do.

The solution came when we weren't even looking for one and in a place we never expected: the Santa Rosa Plaza Mall.

※ ※ ※

In December 2008, we headed up to Santa Rosa Memorial Hospital to join the nurses for their DAISY presentation. To this day we try to visit as many hospitals as we can, and since this was back when we still provided Cinnabons for the DAISY ceremonies, we headed to the store in Santa Rosa Plaza, around the corner from the hospital, to pick them up. The mall was decked out in full Christmas, but as we headed to the food court our eyes were drawn from the familiar decorations and displays to a kiosk selling, of all things, Shona sculpture. We had never seen a kiosk like it anywhere, and we easily spotted the *Mother and Child* for sale.

We panicked. "Mark!" Bonnie exclaimed. "We'd better buy them all. We don't want the nurses to walk in and think they can just buy them at any kiosk in any mall."

Our surprise continued when we reached the kiosk. The retail price for a single sculpture was less than what we were paying in bulk from the gallery. Granted, the gallery's pieces were from established artists whose work sells in galleries, which also slowed production, but we liked these mall versions even more. They felt substantial—two to three times heavier than the gallery's versions. They seemed to be of equal or better quality too, similar in shape, and all were the eight-inch height we wanted but couldn't consistently get.

As we gathered every *Mother and Child* off the shelves, we started chatting with the woman running the kiosk. She told us a guy named John was the kiosk owner. Bonnie gave her our card and asked if she could have John call us. "Why don't you just talk to him now?" she said as she pulled out her phone and dialed. "John, a couple is buying all your mother and children pieces. You want to talk to them?"

And that's how we met John Reynolds.

John had grown up in South Africa during the apartheid era. A white man, he witnessed the incredible disparity between his family's life and the lives of his black countrymen. This deeply troubled him, as he saw the lives of many black Africans up close while doing volunteer work with his church. He decided to leave South Africa. He found a job in California and made a life for himself, but after several years, he felt unfulfilled. He wasn't giving back, and wanted to do something for the Africans he left behind. So he did something about it. He put some money together, flew back to Zimbabwe, bought a bunch of miscellaneous art and trinkets from the artisans who desperately needed the money, and brought it back to sell in the United States. If it worked, he believed he would help himself and the people he bought it from. The art wasn't an instant hit, but in 1996 John's business found its groove and he opened up a 144-square-foot kiosk in the Santa Rosa Plaza. The same one we came upon on our way to pick up Cinnabons.

Bonnie took the phone and told John about DAISY and what we were looking for. He offered to meet us the next day at his storage unit. "I related to their cause," John recalls. "I'm drawn to people that have a higher purpose than just making money. Their story struck a chord in me. That they lost their Patrick was a strong connection. I lost my father when he was just 56."

John didn't have tables in his storage unit so he had laid all the *Mother and Child* sculptures on the floor before we arrived. They looked like a miniature army of mothers and children. Each one was of the same quality we had cleaned out at the mall. We were impressed and ordered 500 pieces. We could have ordered more, but we wanted to

Delivering a large *Healer's Touch* to UCLA Medical Center, Santa Monica, 2010. The three-foot-tall sculptures are bought by organizations for display in their lobbies and healing gardens.

be sure John could deliver. He delivered—every sculpture exactly as promised and on time, the same meticulous consistency and quality as those we saw at his kiosk, and hand-signed by an artist. John also explained to us how unbelievably important that first sale had been to the artists in Zimbabwe.

The year 2008 had been a brutal one in Zimbabwe. The country had been the "bread basket" of Africa, but the government's policies changed all that. In 2008, hyperinflation wasn't simply out of control, it was preposterous. When we met John for the first time that December, Zimbabwe had stopped officially measuring the inflation rate, but estimates had it at 79.6 *billion* percent. Tourism had all but disappeared. The artists John knew were suffering more than his kiosk business could ever help. "DAISY was a lifeline," John says. "It was heartbreaking, but also gratifying. Those first orders saved lives. Today, DAISY is an umbrella of sustenance over the artists—and me."

Over the next year or so, Mark was getting tired of being our shipping department on top of running the financial affairs of the Foundation. He spent his days in his office, packing boxes of pins, certificate portfolios, and our beautiful *Healer's Touch* sculptures. We still tried to go to at least the first presentation at every hospital, so we were traveling like crazy. In 2009, we decided to ask John to work for us 10 hours a week doing shipping. Ten hours soon became 15, and then, as John says, "DAISY was on the runway, took off, and started flying." His team in Zimbabwe grew from six to many, many people working together to deliver the thousands of *Healer's Touches* we would come to need. John loves telling stories of the incredible journey these sculptures make to get into our hands so we can get them into the hands of the nurses, and the power he feels when they finally arrive: "The scene is mesmerizing. It's a vast beautiful ocean of *Healer's Touches* lined up and ready to be packaged with care for DAISY Honorees."

That's the operative word: care. Every person involved in the *Healer's Touch* process cares about and for each other. When Judea, one of the supervising artists John had known for 25 years, died from a heart attack in 2018, we were all devastated. But John told us that an uncle who worked with Judea had taken over and would take care of his wife and family. Because that's the culture of the Shona: If something bad happens to any part of their family, others step in to care for them. That's the culture of the nursing profession as well. It's what DAISY has been built on: caring about others and building relationships. After all, we would never be telling this long *Healer's Touch* story if nurses did not care about us enough to tell others—and then tell us what we meant to them when we needed it most in the years following our aggressive discussion in the summer of 2004.

DAISY HONOREE STORY

Oncology Team Snow Day
UCLA Medical Center Santa Monica
Santa Monica, California

A dying 33-year-old father had a final wish, to take his six-year-old daughter to the snow. That is not an easy request in Southern California. Remarkably, in three short days Snow Day happened and was perfect.

The father had endured two years of treatment including a tandem stem cell transplant and moving his family to L.A. His significant other and daughter were always at his side caring, supporting, and loving him. A cure was not to be and he relapsed less than a month after his stem cell transplant. Heartbroken but determined to live for his daughter, he endured several more months of chemotherapy with little response.

One week before Christmas, this father was admitted to the oncology unit, where everyone loved him and his family. This admission, it was clear that time was short. His daughter was a bright star for her father and all those around her. He held the hand of one of his dedicated nurse healers and said, "I want to take my daughter to the snow." As word spread about this dying wish, the compassion and need to go above and beyond took on a life of its own. Oncology staff started calling, emailing, and texting, and Snow Day was born.

Money for the fifteen tons of snow was found from hospital administration. Money was Venmo-ed for tickets to Disney On Ice for the daughter and her aunt. Snow gloves were purchased, Queen Elsa was found (friend of a nurse's daughter) and many nurses and care partners were off buying "snow" stuff. Oncology staff all around were asking, "What can I do?," "Do you need more money?," and "Can we all come?" Staff put their own holiday plans on hold to make this event possible. This day was about more than snow—it was about dreams, compassion, and our love of our oncology patients. No one at UCLA Santa Monica said "no," but instead said, "What can we do to help?"

Night nurses and care partners set their alarms and dragged themselves out of bed after a few hours of sleep to witness this remarkable day. The day shift was staffed up to allow nurses to rotate down to the party. Staff came with their children and dogs, and many from the hospital came to witness this remarkable event: snow in Southern California. One nurse, too busy to come to the party, took her break later in the day and she and the daughter enjoyed an hour playing in the snow. She could not get enough time in the snow. The attending physician paused rounds and the entire team came to the party.

Respiratory therapy was necessary as the patient was on high-flow oxygen. The therapists planned and practiced how to get him outside for several hours, everyone going above and beyond their workday. Queen Elsa arrived at the patient's room and the daughter was speechless—this was her dream come true. Family members changed the father into his Santa suit, placed him in the wheelchair and two respiratory therapists followed him with carts of oxygen tanks.

The Snow Day reinforced for all the oncology staff that our work is messy, difficult, and the most remarkable nursing that one can do. Our hearts were joyful watching them playing in the snow. None of us will ever forget the day that the oncology staff once again made an amazing difference.

The father died on Christmas morning, his significant other at his side and his daughter with family, waiting for Santa.

"I am a patient advocate first and foremost. It was humbling and special to be honored by my patients. It is very rewarding to be able to be a positive influence in someone's life."

Debbie Zahren Edwards, BSN, RN, CRNI, RN-BC

A Broken Promise

Bonnie's mom was Bea Wain, a big-name big band and radio singer in the 1930s and '40s. (Fun fact: She was the first artist to record "Over the Rainbow," but MGM refused to release it until *The Wizard of Oz* opened and then only released the Judy Garland version.) Mom, or Beazer as Mark called her, passed away in 2017 at the age of 100. Before she died, we went down regularly to see her in Beverly Hills. We would take her out for a steak dinner at the Porterhouse Grill, because that's pretty much all she ate—nothing but meat. No vegetables. No soup. Maybe eggs.

Late one afternoon in 2004, we were out for one of our steak dinners together when a good-looking young waiter introduced himself. With the restaurant mostly empty, Bonnie started making small talk. His name was Damian and like so many Los Angeles waiters, he was trying to make a go of it as an actor in Hollywood. The rest of his story was not so typical. Two years earlier, Damian had left his pregnant wife, Christa, behind in Denver to come to L.A. to study acting and start auditioning. For their anniversary, Christa came to visit, and at just 23 weeks pregnant went into labor and gave birth to their baby boy, Cole. He was whisked to Children's Hospital of Los Angeles. Cole lived all of his first months in the NICU and endured 12 surgeries over most of his first two years. But today Cole was doing great—a happy and energetic kid.

We were in tears as Damian finished his story. Then Bonnie said, "Tell me about the nurses." Damian's face lit up. He said he didn't know what he would have done without their nurses. They basically were Christa's and his family in L.A., given none of their actual family lived in California. "They have been everything to us."

Bonnie smiled. "Would you like to say thank you?"

We explained DAISY to Damian, and he could not have been more excited about the idea of honoring Cole's nurse, Lisa. The next day, Bonnie called the chief nursing officer at Children's Hospital Los Angeles. She got voice mail. "This is Mary Dee Hacker . . ." Bonnie left a message relating the family's desire to say thank you to the nurses who cared for their son and to honor those nurses and many more by bringing DAISY into the hospital. She hung up the phone and wondered how long it would take to hear back—or even if she would. *These calls take time and follow-up*, she thought to herself, remembering what she learned from Bonnie Lasky.

Five minutes later, our phone rang. "Hi Bonnie, this is Mary Dee Hacker. I know exactly who you are. We would love to have the DAISY Award at Children's Hospital Los Angeles." Weeks later, Children's

Hospital Los Angeles became our 27th DAISY hospital. Just over a year after making it, Bonnie had broken her promise to Mark to stop at 50 hospitals—a promise neither of us wanted to keep anymore. Not that we could, even if we did want to keep it. Slowly but surely, DAISY was taking on a life of its own.

"I don't think it was within five minutes, but let's stick with that," says Mary Dee, who retired from Children's Hospital Los Angeles in 2017. She had known about DAISY because it launched in California, and just before Bonnie called, Mary Dee had dinner with Ann Dechairo-Marino, the chief nursing officer at Northridge Medical Center. Ann was the one the year before who asked if we got it, reminded us that it's about the recognition, and compelled us to ditch the dinner and spa treatment gifts. Ann had told Mary Dee all about DAISY.

"The world of CNOs is pretty tight," Mary Dee says. "Back in those days in particular, we all really counted on each other to be our sources of wisdom and clarification and information. To hear about an opportunity to say thank you to the nurses at Children's Hospital, whose hearts are as big as their intelligence—and to have that thank-you coming from outside of us, was something that I considered to be of paramount importance. And the idea of tying it back to the families and children we serve was a dimension that we didn't have in our toolbox at Children's Hospital Los Angeles. We can create all kinds of things within our organization, and we do. But the most meaningful things have always come from people on the outside who say, 'I want to help honor that.' They see what I can't. I'm not watching nurses at three o'clock in the morning. I can't be in every room. So the decision to bring in DAISY wasn't complicated. It was: 'Yes, please, help me thank and appreciate these people who come to their jobs each day with a commitment to help from both a clinical standpoint, as well as from a human connection standpoint.'" You can never thank people enough in life, but this is especially true for nurses who every day come to work in emotionally challenging environments. No matter where they are, how big the organization, and who they serve, nurses are, as Mary Dee says, "forever present. They are with patients and families during the most challenging times of their lives, and they are there with clinical knowledge and a caring heart."

There was another reason that made Mary Dee believe that DAISY would be a perfect fit for the culture of Children's Hospital Los Angeles: Its devotion to the concept of family- or patient-centered care, that is, listening to, involving, and informing patients when it comes to their care and clinical decisions. Mary Dee first read about this concept when she was an undergraduate student in Minnesota in the late 1960s. The work came out of Children's Hospital Los Angeles but was dismissed as West Coast "crazy" by many of her nursing teachers and colleagues. "Back in those days, it was very much believed that nursing was more of a technical expertise rather than a caring art. But Children's Hospital Los Angeles has clearly understood and embraced a sense of humanity in providing care. DAISY not only fit our culture really well but enhanced it."

That Mary Dee believed this and got the power of recognition and gratitude—and got that DAISY got it, too—energized all of us. We sprang into action. We arranged for the first DAISY Award at Children's Hospital Los Angeles to be given in October 2004 to Cole's nurse, Lisa Coffman. Simultaneously, Mary Dee looked for someone to run DAISY who had the time and would embrace its value, even if that value was just beginning to be understood by nurses and hospitals. As it so happened that the day Mary Dee announced to her team she was bringing DAISY in, she was having a retirement party for Marion Antoku. A nurse at Children's for 40-plus years, Marion had also been Mary Dee's manager when she was starting out. Mary Dee knew Marion would do a fabulous job running DAISY, connect to it, and have time to do it right.

It was Marion who greeted us in the lobby when we arrived at the hospital with Damian, Christa, and Cole for the first award. She handed us our security badges and walked with us toward the room where the presentation would take place. We thought Cole would be screaming, crying, and a nervous wreck, not wanting to be at the place he had been in and out of constantly for two years. Wrong. Cole was just as Damian described him: happy and energetic. Being at Children's was like he was at the playground. He kept moving and smiling, pointing out things on the wall and showing us rooms and, of course, the toy bins.

And then we got to the room for the presentation and Cole saw Lisa. He ran across the floor to her and gave her the biggest hug. The rest of the event was a beautiful and joyful celebration. All the powers that be at Children's Hospital Los Angeles were there. We left knowing DAISY was in the best hands. But what lingers in our memory today was that hug from little Cole to his nurse, Lisa.

As we always say, nurses give the best hugs but when those hugs meet the hug of a grateful and loving child, words fail to capture the feeling.

Lisa Coffman's name was the first added to a DAISY Award plaque that would be permanently mounted in a public hallway at Children's Hospital Los Angeles with room to add many more names. To find those names for the next awards, Mary Dee and Marion established a committee and put out a call for nominations. Moving forward, they decided that as at many hospitals, the awards would be given as surprises to the nurses. But Children's extended that surprise to everyone in the units where the nurses worked. Mary Dee and Marion also decided to invite the honoree's family members to make the surprise even more powerful—a complicated process but so worth it for the DAISY Honorees in their opinion. What neither Mary Dee nor Marion counted on was that the hospital would get so many nominations that the selection committee of nurses was overwhelmed by its success.

"I think that DAISY grew organically in hospitals in its first years, so it took a while for the communication and the value of it to be shared," recalls Mary Dee, who years later joined our board. "CNOs are busy, but my lens was that anything I can do to raise nurses up and say thank you, I want to be doing." Turns out, others had started to see through that same lens and understand the importance of building a culture of recognition in the organization. This came into sharper focus for us that same fall when DAISY received its first cold call.

❀ ❀ ❀

"This is Ann Evans," the voice on the other end of the phone said as soon as Bonnie picked up the phone. "Are you for real?" Anyone who knows Ann knows this is exactly what she said. Ann was then vice president and chief of patient care services at Tallahassee Memorial Hospital and cold-called us after reading about DAISY in the July 2004 American Organization of Nurse Executives (AONE) newsletter. Ann had been president of the American Association of Critical-Care Nurses (AACN). She was well aware of the landmark work AACN was undertaking on the essentials of a healthy work environment, one of which was meaningful recognition of nurses. But even before AACN published their research in 2005, Ann saw something meaningful in the recognition DAISY offered. After assuring her we indeed were for real and having a delightful conversation, we booked a flight to Florida to get DAISY going. And very soon, it was going.

Despite the Mary Dee and Ann Evans experiences, in early 2005 it didn't look like Bonnie was going to break her promise to Mark. We added fewer hospitals in 2004 (10) than in 2003 (11) and finished the year with a total of 28. But what started with Mary Dee and Ann Evans really started to roll in the next few years. Sure, Bonnie was still cold calling, but more and more people answered those calls to action, including donors. Shortly after meeting Damian, Bonnie ran into her former assistant from her advertising days, Jonathan Weedman, who had become the head of the Wells Fargo Foundation in Los Angeles. She explained DAISY and asked if he wanted to sponsor the awards at Children's Hospital for a $1,000 donation to cover the costs. He gave us $2,000 and told us to always ask for double what something costs when dealing with a corporate sponsor—that way even if you can't use it to spread more good in the world, you can still cover what you need if you get less!

The chance encounter with Jonathan underscored for us once again the power of lasting relationships—not just for DAISY but for life in general. That was certainly true for the health of DAISY. Our relationships with nurses and their relationships with each other were fundamental to DAISY's growth.

Ann Evans eventually brought dozens of hospitals and a few industry partners to DAISY, and she joined our board. Mary Dee Hacker also joined our board and didn't just build the future for

DAISY at Children's. She made it her mission to get other children's hospitals to adopt DAISY. "CNOs of the children's hospitals in the country meet twice a year together, and it's a really tight community," Mary Dee says. "We share practice. We strive hard to reduce harm and injury and improve care. So we're collaborative, not competitive, and at those meetings, I talked about the DAISY Award and recognition, and I invited those CNOs to become part of it and that was effective. It was that simple."

In May 2005, Beth Heyman, who ran DAISY at Health Alliance of Greater Cincinnati, wrote to us after our visit to talk about and present the DAISY Award at one of her hospitals: "I am still caught up in the emotional (both personal and professional) high you brought to Cincinnati. I thank you for your time and commitment to something you obviously believe in with your hearts. YOU made ME proud to be a nurse! If I lived closer to you I would give you all my time for your cause to use in any way you needed." She committed to getting us 10 more hospital contacts in Ohio and beyond. She said she, her family, and her nursing network had already pitched DAISY to several hospitals in Chicago. She was ready to "nudge," she said. "I am taking up the cause." (Beth later became dean of the Galen College of Nursing in Cincinnati and joined our board. In 2007, she launched the discussion that later led to DAISY adding nursing faculty to our awards: "Someone had to teach those nurses who took such great care of your son Patrick.")

In 2006, Susan Grant, who had been the chief nursing officer at the University of Washington Medical Center when we presented our first DAISY Award, became the system chief nurse executive at Emory Health in Atlanta and quickly brought DAISY to all three hospitals in the system at the time. "In healthcare, we know very well as nurses, as physicians, as administrators, we do not build the patient and family voice into everything we do," Susan says. "We look through the lens of an administrator or a healthcare professional and that's not always a lens that considers what patients and families think. The whole goal for my being brought into Emory was advancing patient- and family-centered care and elevating nursing to achieve Magnet designation in our different hospitals. But there wasn't really a framework for professional practice that was consistently applied across the hospitals. So I used DAISY as a tool for people to start to paint the canvas of what professional practice looks like."

To achieve this, Susan opened up DAISY nominations from not only patients and families, but also staff and other professionals. She and other administrators would read those nominations out loud to nursing staff across the hospitals so they could hear what professional practice looks like. She made meaningful recognition part of Emory's transformation model. Like we have heard from so many chief nursing officers, DAISY gave Susan a genuine story rather than just numbers from satisfaction surveys that don't tell you anything about what those numbers mean. Susan wasn't looking for data or compliance numbers. She was looking for something that nurses could build on and grow and learn from.

"I could talk about holding ourselves to high standards of care, using the Magnet framework," Susan says. "But those are just words from a nurse administrator. The nurses probably are thinking, 'I know she believes in what she's talking about and it sounds really good, but I have no idea what that actually means or looks like in practice.' Using the DAISY nominations and reading them as exemplars of outstanding nursing practice that were in the words of patients and of families—in the words of their colleagues—that showed what outstanding practice actually looks like. . . . Everybody got it and could relate to it. And before you knew it there were nursing practice councils on units that were holding themselves to that vision. DAISY empowers nurses to kind of carry that vision and continue to evolve it instead of it being this top-down nurse administrator saying, 'Here, I'm going to tell you how to do this and what it's going to look like.' Nurses create it."

Stories like Susan's, Mary Dee's, Beth's, and Ann Evans's are the main reason that after adding only 49 hospitals in its first five years, DAISY added 133 in its next two. Every hospital we added brought another one, two, five—not just from its own system but thanks to the relationships between nurses. Nurses were also moving from hospital to hospital and bringing DAISY with them. As Susan said, DAISY was being *owned* by the nurses, and that could not have delighted us more.

It was why when we added our 50th hospital in January 2006, we knew we couldn't stop, Bonnie's promise to Mark notwithstanding. We sailed past 50 hospitals to more than 100 by mid-2007.

Problem was, we had no infrastructure, no database, to support all this growth. Suddenly we felt like we were drowning. It was 2007. DAISY was approaching 200 hospitals. Mark was doing all our shipping from a guest room in our house. Bonnie was doing the paperwork by hand from another room we converted to an office. All day long she heard his tape gun going, packing pins, certificate portfolios, and *Healer's Touch* sculptures. It was a happy sound . . . and completely overwhelming. Something had to give or we never would have made it to 2008 and met John Reynolds in that mall. DAISY was getting expensive—more expensive than we could possibly sustain even with the generosity of our donors. We were just full-time volunteers, paying for our own travel and most DAISY expenses. If we didn't do something, DAISY would soon be a victim of its own success.

While we built our board and figured out what to do, the nurses not only drove DAISY forward, they lifted us up with their words and their stories of compassionate care.

DAISY HONOREE STORY

Donna Marzullo, BSN, RN, Step Down Advocate
Advocate Christ Medical Center
Oak Lawn, Illinois

Often you hear the phrases such as "nurses are heroes," "nurses are hard workers," and "nurses are so smart," but most often heard characteristic of nurses are that they are the most understanding and most compassionate people on earth. Not only are nurses equipped with a vast knowledge of medicine, but nurses also care for patients holistically. Donna Marzullo is not only one of the hardest working nurses, she is also the most compassionate and thoughtful human being.

Donna has always had the biggest heart. Since she began working on the unit many years ago, Donna and her two daughters have gone out of their way to ensure that the patients have a wonderful holiday. Knowing that our patients will have to spend Christmas in the hospital made Donna and her daughters very sad. They decided that they wanted to do something to cheer them up! Every year, Donna and her two daughters buy the materials to make blankets, using money that comes out of their own pockets. They make 17 handmade fleece blankets and come into Advocate Christ Medical Center on Christmas to deliver them to each patient. Donna and her daughters take the time to wish each patient a "Merry Christmas" as they place their warm, fuzzy new blanket over them. Many patients and their families verbalized how receiving a Christmas gift not only made them feel good but also made them feel like they were spending Christmas at home. Many people had tears in their eyes. Patients were amazed by Donna and her daughters and so grateful for their thoughtfulness and generosity.

Another time, Donna was caring for a very confused patient who was impulsive. Donna and her fellow nurse came up with a clever way to safely distract the patient. They gave the patient a "job" for the day. The patient was asked to "stamp" a few envelopes. He also carefully folded linen for the staff. While believing they did an excellent job redirecting him in a safe manner, little did they know that it would backfire on them. At the end of his "shift," the patient asked for his payment! Donna, out of the goodness of her heart, paid the patient $10 out of her own pocket. She made him very happy and told him that he was one of her best employees. The look on the confused patient's face was priceless. He was very proud of the great job he did. Again, this was just another "Donna" thing to do from her very caring heart.

In her most recent act of kindness, Donna bought her patient lunch, using her own money. This patient had recently received a devastating diagnosis and was not coping well. The patient was also very upset as he said the kitchen continued to send him trays that he did not order. Donna took the patient's order and bought him lunch from the cafeteria. The patient and his wife were so incredibly thankful for Donna. The wife stated that she was so grateful that Donna bought her husband lunch and that this small act of caring meant more than she could ever know. The patient's wife stated, "Knowing that Donna is caring for my husband, I can now go home for the night and can sleep peacefully in my bed knowing that my husband is well taken care of."

Patients, families, peers, and physicians go on and on about how wonderful Donna is and how her heart is bursting with love. She is a team player and an amazing, compassionate nurse. Donna cares for her patients' minds, bodies, and souls. Donna exhibits empathy in all situations and truly cares about each and every patient she cares for. She is an outstanding role model for the nursing profession!

Note: This is Donna's second DAISY Award!

"Though I honestly don't feel like what I did was extraordinary, receiving the award was probably the most touching acknowledgment I will ever receive as a nurse."

Rebecca Johnson, RN

The Power of Stories and Gratitude

I grew up on a dairy farm with seven siblings. My parents said if we wanted to go on to college we would have to pay our own way. Wanting to be a nurse from childhood, I worked as a nurse aide for several years and saved my money to go to nursing school. When I went to pay my admissions fee, I found they had raised tuition significantly, and I didn't have enough money to enter the program. My dad said he would somehow work something out to get the money. A few weeks later, he took me back to the school and put down the remaining money needed. It was only when we got home that I realized he and Mother had sold our prize milk cow to get the money. The cow's name was Daisy. When I heard Bonnie and Mark's story, I loved the idea of yet another way to recognize my nursing staff. But the name Daisy held a special place in my heart.

We have loved that story since the day we heard Jane Swaim, then the chief nursing officer at St. Elizabeth's Healthcare, tell it to us in 2007. Truth is, we had to reach out to her to get the story again when we were writing this book. We were bad at recording any stories back then. We didn't start featuring DAISY Honorees and their nominations on our website until that same year. Our early nomination forms and many of those from our partner hospitals didn't have much room for those stories, either. Some of them were just a small sheet of paper you tore from a pad. To help sustain our program, we asked our participating hospitals to create their own criteria that fit their culture under the banner of compassionate care, which is what DAISY was established to recognize. So many of the hospitals' criteria were things like positive attitude, meeting patient and family needs, collaborating with the healthcare team, and interpersonal skills. But then the form had just a line or three for an explanation. They read, well, clinically. Some didn't even use the word compassion, despite our mission. As a result, a lot of the early nominations went something like, "Mary was a wonderful nurse. She went above and beyond to take care of us during this time."

We didn't get the rich details we have today until we evolved the forms, and then pushed every hospital to make stories the priority. Honestly, we weren't very good at pushing for nominations, let alone stories, in our first years. In fact, the nurses were the ones who pointed the way for much of what we include when organizations sign up for DAISY. First came the idea for a banner, from Providence St. Vincent's Hospital in Portland, Oregon. After Bonnie stopped crying the first time she saw it, we started working on giving one to all our hospitals. Then a hospital in Michigan started giving a pin, which they designed, to every nurse who got a nomination. Being trained in advertising and marketing, we also shared that idea. (Bonnie prefers that Mark use the

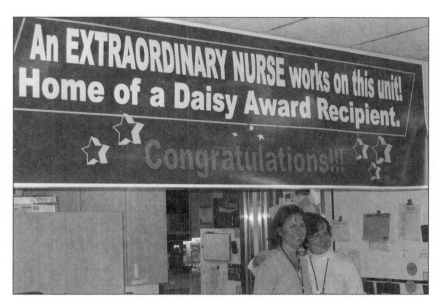

Providence St. Vincent's Hospital in Portland, OR created the first DAISY banner in 2004. They may have spelled DAISY lowercase, but Bonnie still cried tears of joy when she saw it.

"Stolen" Idea: Our first version of the now-coveted DAISY banner displayed at a DAISY Award presentation at Cincinnati Children's Hospital, 2006

term "share" rather than "stole" but the result was the same. Later, we share-stole that same hospital's design for a pin for nurses who had been nominated several times.)

A real turning point for us was when we visited OSF Saint Francis Medical Center in Peoria, Illinois, which was getting thousands of nominations a year. (We knew because they kept ordering nominee pins.) We asked how they were doing it. The nurses walked us into a patient room and there was a sign with daisies and a big bold headline: THANK YOUR NURSE. Below that the words continued: FOR OUTSTANDING CARE. It then asked people to complete a DAISY Award nomination form and where to find it. Bonnie's a born and bred New Yorker, and even she thought this was pushy. But then we realized maybe we were being too reserved. Even if a sign like that didn't lead to a nomination, it could at least lead to a thank-you, which we much later realized *our own materials did not say*. Yes, it was a real head-slapping moment in DAISY's existence to recognize our first signs did not say THANK YOUR NURSE—in spite of the fact that we were so grateful, and countless nurses told us DAISY was creating a culture of gratitude as well as recognition. It even built bridges between mortal enemies: One nurse told us that despite being a proud Michigan State Spartan, the DAISY Award from her colleagues at the University of Michigan hospital made "a place in [her] heart for those of you who are Wolverines."

Today we can't say thank you enough to nurses for being nurses, even if those nurses think that they are "not doing anything special." So we thank them for "just doing your job." For making the world a better place by staying true to the importance of caring in healing—a principle to which nurses commit when they join this noble profession. But in 2007, we were just waking up to the larger importance of saying thank you along with the power of the nomination stories.

Like we said, however, many nurses and more and more hospitals like OSF Saint Francis already understood this. They were using DAISY to enhance and even build their cultures of recognition and gratitude by honoring more than just clinical excellence or some management-selected employee-of-the-month program. They understood the power of stories describing compassionate care. If we needed more of a reminder of just how powerful those DAISY stories and moments of gratitude had become, around the same time as we heard the Daisy cow story, Susan Grant invited us to Emory for a special event.

❀ ❀ ❀

Susan knew we'd come. We tried to attend every event we were invited to (and many we weren't), and we never missed an opportunity to get to Atlanta, because it meant seeing Tena and Riley, who lived there. But Susan had planned something new that made this visit even more exciting. After a year of presenting DAISY Awards at Emory's three hospitals, she arranged for a breakfast with the honorees, many of whom did not know each other and had never met us. They were, however, used to Susan and other leaders reading DAISY nominations aloud as part of developing Emory's professional best practices.

But if the nurses thought that Susan was going to read their stories at the breakfast, they were wrong. As we gathered around the table, Susan asked the nurses themselves to go around the room and tell everyone what they were nominated for. We weren't surprised what happened next.

One of the biggest changes from DAISY's first years had been the willingness of nurses to nominate each other for the DAISY Awards. We got exactly zero nominations from nurses at our first hospital. That changed as they saw the value in the meaningful recognition DAISY offered. Nurses may not see themselves as unsung heroes, but more and more they saw it in each other, especially in the smallest details. They know that little things can make a big difference in their patients' care and outcomes, because there are no little things to patients when it comes to their care and outcomes.

What had *not* changed—and this remains true to this day—was what we captured in how we say thank you to nurses: They are not only shocked by their nominations but feel they have done nothing special to earn them. Nurses feel they're doing this good work because it's who they are. They may be proud of their DAISY Awards, but pride doesn't make them see what they did as impressive, or great at talking about it. That inability was on full display at Emory that morning. After the first nurse self-consciously told her story of being nominated by her patient, the nurse who followed said, "Wow, that's an incredible story. I didn't do anything like that." When she was done, the third nurse said. "Well of course you both got the DAISY Award. I didn't do anything like them. . . . " And so it went. All the way around the room—every nurse just as self-effacing as the last.

Their stories that morning varied in the size and scope of their compassionate care: some grand gestures, some moments of profound intimacy; some acts that happened over the course of an hour, some that played out over weeks and months. Still not one of those nurses saw themselves as doing anything impressive—anything more than what they do every day. But by the time the last nurse spoke, they had to know the emotion that their stories elicited in the room, and that the admiration for them was profound. Everyone at the table was in tears. Okay, Susan cries when you say hello to her, but this time we and all the nurses were with her. They had to know how much they had made a difference. What they might not have known is how much they—and hundreds before them—had been making a difference to *us*.

The certificate each DAISY Honoree receives reads: "In deep appreciation of all you do, who you are, and the incredibly meaningful difference you make in the lives of so many people." We accept that many of our honorees have no idea how special they were to their patients, how much they have made a difference to patients and to other nurses. We can't try to convince them any more than we already have. But we can tell them what a difference their stories and words made to us.

As we worked to figure out the next chapter in DAISY's story, it was stories like those we heard at Emory and words of thanks from the DAISY Honorees across the country that kept us going—and opened us up to changing our story and the entire way DAISY operated.

One nurse gave a shave and a haircut to a homeless man after he passed away so that his parents, who hadn't seen him in several years, would see him for who he was and not what he had become.

One nurse washed the hair of a teenage girl so she could look nice when her friends came to visit her in the hospital.

One helped a suicidal patient see clearly.

One painted a snowy picture of the community church and put up Christmas decorations for the patient who was that church's pastor and was lonely for his congregation during the holiday.

One made sure "Tigger" and "Bun Bun" were in the recovery room when a young patient woke up from surgery.

One pushed a patient to fight through the pain and get out of bed and do his exercises after open heart surgery; came back on her day off and refused to leave until he got out of bed; and was waiting for him with a hug when he reached the end of the hall weeks later.

One helped a seven-year-old through a bone marrow transplant.

One brought in her son to play the violin for a patient who loved music.

One went through the garbage in the basement to find a patient's treasure when environmental services thought it was trash.

One snuck in a terminal patient's golden retriever so he could say goodbye to his best friend and companion of 11 years.

One made sure there was always clothes for patients who lacked them.

One gave a patient the sneakers off his feet.

One gave a man a cross when he most needed it.

One—and this is one of Mark's favorites—checked with the doctor and then went to the store for some gin and vermouth to make the perfect martini so a couple, married for 64 years, could enjoy a drink together while the wife was in the hospital.

One nurse put all these DAISY moments and countless more in perspective for us: "It's the small things that you do every day, the things you take for granted that matter so much. It's taking the time to be with parents when you are way behind on your paperwork. It's being a friend and support system to a very young family, helping a mom understand that it's okay for her baby to leave this world and then have her tell you that you made it bearable for her. It's helping the sibling of a baby understand why their brother or sister is sick. It could be as simple as starting an IV for another nurse. At that moment you become their heroes."

And ours.

Those examples we listed are of course just fragments of stories we've heard about the work of DAISY Honorees, almost all of them from the early years of DAISY that revealed the impact nurses had on their patients. They came to us long before we asked for them for our records and our website. They also held us together the first eight years along with the letters we got from those nurses thanking us for the DAISY Award. We got form letters from the places we donated to that support ITP research and patients, but we received hundreds of handwritten heartfelt thank-you's from nurses. Those and the memory of Patrick drove us forward, each one like a hug in the mail. Every summer when Riley came to visit, she would make scrapbooks of them. Stacks of them filled Mark's office, and do to this day.

We also started getting scrapbooks from hospitals and nurses too, many with daisies and hand-colored decorations on their pages. The first really big scrapbook we got was from Children's Hospital Los Angeles from Mary Dee's staff. Memorial Sloan Kettering Cancer Center in New York City sent us a photo book they made online with pictures from their first award, too, something they later did for every nurse. The chief nursing officer at San Francisco General had the scrapbook her nurses maintained of all their DAISY Award honorees on the table outside her office. It was the only thing the nurses who came in to interview with her could look at.

One from Mercy San Juan Medical Center in Sacramento given to us in 2004 had a picture of Patrick on the cover and these words beneath it: "Patrick's wings have lifted many a weary nurse's spirit."

The power of these words did more than just make us emotional. They did more than help us fight through the years we struggled. They did more than strengthen our resolve. They made us change our focus. Until 2005, DAISY still listed ITP organizations we supported in our newsletters. But as the overwhelming response from the nurses we knew and the thousands we did not filled our home, their words showed us not only what DAISY meant to them but also how DAISY worked for

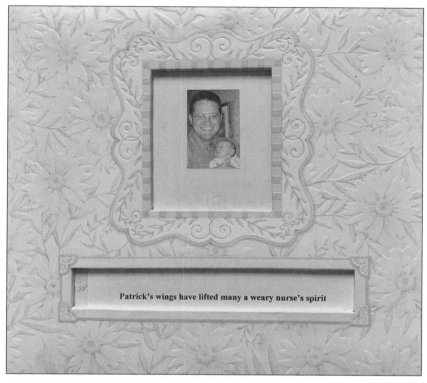

"Patrick's wings have lifted many a weary nurse's spirit." The cover of a scrapbook given to us by Mercy San Juan Medical Center, Sacramento, 2004

them, and what was of value to them. The nurses were refining DAISY for us, bringing it front and center. We needed to be all in on the DAISY Awards; we had to focus on the nurses and drop almost everything else. So while we occasionally supported ITP causes personally—not as DAISY—after 2005, DAISY effectively became about the nurses that year.

Not that nurses weren't always our love. (Why else would Bonnie spend so much time cold calling and arranging gifts?) But after a bumpy start, the nurses had gone from *a* focus to *the* focus. Nurses owned DAISY; we were the facilitators. The 2007 DAISY brochure that replaced our homemade newsletter captured this complete swing to nurses:

Since DAISY's inception, we've found ourselves focusing more of our resources, time, and frankly, affection on the DAISY Award than on the other goals. The level of acceptance and appreciation by hospitals has astounded and gratified us. Hospital administrators view the DAISY Award not only as a way to acknowledge outstanding nursing, but also as a strategic tool in managing the nurse shortage that threatens the heart of our healthcare system. Nurses who experienced DAISY presentations are moved and motivated by them. We are very proud of the program's accomplishments for nurses and will work to continue its expansion into more and more hospitals. Patrick would've loved this!

Patrick would also have loved that DAISY was growing more than ever before in 2007, now approaching 200 hospitals and 1,500 DAISY presentations a year. What Patrick would not have loved was the fact that even if we didn't grow any more, we would soon run out of money. We were giving our program as a gift to our hospitals and doing some creative fundraising to add to the significant amount of money we were spending out of our own pocket, like hosting a grape harvest wine weekend at our home for two couples that we sold at an auction every year. But it was hard work. We had tapped our own networks for too long. And we still didn't know that many people in the healthcare industry who would donate. Something had to change.

Evidence for our statement about how nurse leaders viewed DAISY was not merely anecdotal. In 2007, we knew dozens of hospitals saw DAISY as beneficial for retention, recruitment, morale, and more. With DAISY growing so rapidly, the year before we had decided to do a detailed survey of our hospital partners to better understand them and how and why they were using the program. We sent a DAISY Award questionnaire to all our hospitals. The eight-page survey asked questions like how frequently they gave out the DAISY Award, how many they had given in the past year, what criteria the hospital used, who could nominate the nurses, whether the hospital had Magnet designation, whether it used the banner we were then providing to them, how DAISY supported the hospital's values, and if we were beneficial for retention. We also asked to see their nomination forms. We received more than 100 responses.

As we combed through them all, we were gratified that so many engaged with DAISY on a deeper level, while the responses from the few that struggled to sustain DAISY confirmed what we suspected: They didn't have the awards embedded in their culture, something we had stressed almost since the beginning. Overall, few of the answers surprised us, except the answers on page six, which focused on our future. Actually, we thought the questions would surprise the hospitals first. Not the one at the top of the page that asked if they planned to continue the DAISY Award in 2007. Even hospitals struggling to embed the award were still committed to DAISY, which has been the case throughout our existence. Only one hospital had dropped the program by 2006, and we have maintained a high retention rate in our first 20 years: excluding hospitals that have closed or merged with others, 96 percent of the more than 4,000 organizations that started presenting the DAISY Award still do.

No, the most surprising question was actually preceded by a one-paragraph explanation under the bold, underlined header "Finally . . . ":

A number of our hospitals have asked us how we fund The DAISY Award and how they might be supportive. We are quite creative with our fundraising. Today, we have been able to support the program financially with the help of Family and Corporate Sponsors so we can provide the program to you at no charge. However, now that we are expanding so rapidly and have a long-term plan for The DAISY Award's growth, we may *at some time in the future ask you to help us by contributing to the cost of The DAISY Award at your hospital or directing us to a Sponsor who can underwrite the cost for you. So we would appreciate your insight by answering just a few more questions.*

The first question asked how much money chief nursing officers felt would be a reasonable contribution to help us keep the award going at their hospitals. The second asked how long it would take to get that contribution approved in their budgets. We stressed that we were not asking for commitment, simply trying to gauge the hospitals' interest and ability to support the program in the future. We gave them choices of $1,000, $2,000, and $5,000 or more a year as well as the ability to say they couldn't contribute.

Bonnie thought few would say they would pay for something they had been getting for free since the beginning. She was concerned that asking organizations to pay was a violation of our mission and the trust nurse leaders had put in us. She had said as much to her friend Lynne Doll, who had sponsored our third hospital, Cedars-Sinai in Los Angeles. Lynne had introduced UnitedHealthcare as a corporate sponsor for select hospitals they wanted to support. But the company wanted the hospitals to pay for DAISY after one year of corporate sponsorship. That had launched the conversation of the hospitals paying, but Bonnie told the board she didn't like asking, nor did she believe anyone would pay. But she also knew we had no choice unless she wanted to go into full-blown fundraiser mode (which she surely did not). DAISY was growing unsustainably in the hands of the nurses, but we couldn't support them much longer with us paying—a big reason she thought so many of them were signing up. "I didn't want to start charging them because I had worked so hard to get them," Bonnie recalls. "I made all those cold calls. I had been up against people saying, 'Are you for real? Nurses don't need it.' We had gotten all these hospitals to take the program, and I was afraid it would look like a bait and switch."

We got that it was about the recognition, but did nurses and hospitals value that recognition enough to completely reverse how it was funded? Mark had already reversed his opinion. At the time of our aggressive discussion three years earlier, he had wanted to control growth. "And thankfully we did a pretty crappy job of it," he admits, because DAISY was poised to keep growing and growing and growing. Now Mark said if we wanted to grow, we should *grow*—more than just the organic word-of-mouth growth we were experiencing. We knew there was an opportunity to make DAISY bigger than we ever imagined, but we needed to be more strategic. We needed help and support to seize that opportunity. The worst thing that could happen would be having to start turning nurses away and not be able to provide. Bonnie had stopped doing cold calls, but we were getting more calls than we could possibly handle or afford. Mark the entrepreneur had built an organization and said it clearly to Bonnie: "We need to run DAISY like a business." A growing one, not the struggling one from a few years ago. We had zero customer acquisition costs, but we needed help with customer service and fulfillment. We needed a database and a CFO. And we needed money. Would the hospitals be willing to pay?

When the answers to the question about shifting the financial responsibility to the hospitals came in, none—not even the struggling hospitals—checked the box beside "Sorry, we cannot contribute anything." Most of them said they would contribute $2,000—more than we would need to provide them with a monthly award. Some said they would pay more. They saw our value. But Bonnie still took some convincing to shift her mindset—these answers on our questionnaire weren't commitments to pay, just promises. Who finally convinced Bonnie to do so, told us what we needed to do, and then helped us change our story for good? A nurse, of course—the head of one of America's most prestigious nursing organizations. The first organization to help us completely understand the value in our concept and how far we had come from just wanting to say thank you to nurses for the extraordinary care we experienced during Our Patrick's hospitalization in 1999.

DAISY HONOREE STORY

Joan Horton, RN
University of Kansas Medical Center
Kansas City, Kansas

The DAISY Award recognizes the unsung heroes who walk among us. That is, our nurses. One of our nurses recognizes the unsung heroes [who] walk among our patients. This nurse goes above and beyond to honor patients who served in the military.

Joan Horton is an experienced emergency nurse. She knows that patients who walk or roll through the emergency room doors are at a significant disadvantage. Not only are they sick or injured, but some come from underserved populations; they may be homeless, frightened, scared, alone, in pain—the list goes on. To make matters worse, one of the first things we do is take their clothes away. So much dignity is lost in a matter of minutes!

Joan knows how to bridge the gap. Although Joan's first priority is to make sure every patient is stable, she doesn't just physically assess her patients. She listens . . . almost with her heart. And her heart almost always recognizes patients with a military background. It might be the "yes ma'am" that she hears when she asks if they are taking medications or maybe the fact they look at her directly in the eye during the conversation. Sometimes she sees a tattoo. That's when she knows that on another day, this patient was well and dedicated to serving our country.

Joan understands military service and sacrifice. And she shows her respect for it. Joan carries "thank-you" cards for military members. She has these made at her own expense and rarely mentions them to her coworkers. Although small, the card carries a powerful message that acknowledges the individual's fight for the freedom of others who haven't had to fight for their own freedom. The card also expresses gratitude for the individual's service to country. The level of respect that this action conveys is huge! It immediately helps overcome some of the disadvantages the sick or injured patient feels in the moment. The card shows the patient that Joan sees them not just as a sick person worthy of her care and compassion, but as a hero worthy of her respect.

To me, it signifies the beginning of a special bond that I know Joan's unsung hero patients feel towards her.

"Watching the emotion on each nurse's face when he/she hears their nomination story is heartwarming. The true passion of this profession is evident through each of these encounters."

Greg Opseth, BSN, RN, MHA

Funding Our Future

While Bonnie still did not believe the solution to DAISY's financial future was making hospitals pay for the award, we both knew DAISY needed help—help we could not provide or figure out ourselves. So we asked our board what to do. By our summer 2007 retreat, DAISY's board had changed considerably from our first years when it was just family and friends. Tena and Dianne were still part of it, but we now had more than a dozen nurses and other professionals advising us, including Cindy Angiulo (University of Washington), Mary Dee Hacker (Children's Hospital Los Angeles), Ann Evans (who had moved to Exempla Lutheran Medical Center in Colorado), Beth Heyman (from what was then called the Health Alliance of Greater Cincinnati), Jane Kamstra (CHRISTUS Santa Rosa), and Bonnie Lasky (University of California at San Francisco). These people traced the history of DAISY's evolution, and their relationships with us had been essential to our growth. Who better to help us chart a path forward than those who could represent the nurses we felt already owned the meaning of DAISY?

The board was united in its suggestion for whom to approach for that help: Pam Thompson, head of the American Organization of Nurse Executives (AONE), the largest professional organization for nurse leaders in the world (renamed the American Organization for Nursing Leadership or AONL in 2019). AONE could provide some insight into our business plan, administrative support, and maybe resources. We needed to ask Pam to partner DAISY and AONE.

We knew of AONE, of course. Many of the chief nursing officers and other nurse leaders with whom we worked were members, and we had been featured in its newsletter *Voice of Nursing Leadership* three years earlier. We knew the organization had marketing muscle, but we didn't need marketing. We didn't need an email blast or another article. We needed a partner. The question was: Did they? Would Pam even know who we were, and respond? There was only one way to find out. AONE had offices in Washington, DC and Chicago. Cindy said she was close to the Northwest board member, Patti Crome, and would ask her to connect us to Pam. Cindy knew Pam too, but she felt we would have a better chance of getting Pam's attention if a board member made the introduction. Cindy reached out and Patti immediately agreed to forward what we sent. Bonnie was about to write the most important email of DAISY's life.

"I will never forget writing that email," Bonnie says. "I did feel it was the most important thing I was ever going to do for DAISY, and I had one shot to do it. I went through draft after draft with Mark. We slaved over it. We thought through every word, hoping our passion for nurses would come across as strongly as we felt it. Finally we let it go."

We could only pray that Pam would respond.

❋ ❋ ❋

When Bonnie's email hit Pam's desk, she had no idea who we were. "My recognition of DAISY when Bonnie contacted me? None," says Pam. But that didn't keep her from reading what the board member had passed on: "You never know what opportunities are out there. And what DAISY had was something that we highly supported: recognizing nurses at the bedside." The human touch, the part that can't be taught from a manual like the technology and clinical side. "That's a key, important role of delivering excellent nursing care," Pam adds. "Our membership are the leaders in organizations, but they also respect the fact that the person that is at the bedside delivers the care. You can't have a good nursing department if you don't have excellence at the bedside. And so it definitely fit within one of our goals of recognizing it in a more authentic way. When Bonnie's email explained to us what she was doing, that authenticity was absolutely there. For me, DAISY represented the essence of the arts of our profession."

Pam also understood that DAISY did more than any employee-of-the-month could ever hope to do. To her, our authenticity wasn't just in the DAISY mission, but the nominations coming from the people we served—or equally as powerfully, other nurses. That sparked her interest the most. AONE had a strong commitment not only to patient-centered care but also to shared governance, defined by the American Association for Nursing Development as "a structure and process for partnership, equity, accountability, and ownership. It puts the responsibility, authority, and accountability for practice-related decisions into the hands of the individuals who will operationalize the decision."

"When DAISY reached out, AONE was working on making sure that people understood the concepts of shared governance and incorporated that into the work that they were doing," Pam recalls. "And the whole foundation of shared governance is shared leadership. What better way to recognize your colleagues then colleague to colleague? Yes there were a lot of places that were experimenting with employee engagement from the perspective of a "best employee" award and doing things like that. But they were top down. That's really important to note that. To have patients and nurses recognize it and be inspired by the care that a patient received? DAISY had all the good markings of a program that could do the right thing for nurses at the bedside in a very meaningful way. They were also very mission driven and grounded—you don't find that very often. All that intrigued me about them."

But Pam wasn't going to just offer the help of AONE sight unseen. She wanted to talk with DAISY and understand our goals and how she and AONE could help. For Pam, it was about the fit between the two, something DAISY certainly understood. It was why we made the awards both turnkey and adaptable to fit any hospital's culture. "DAISY wasn't asking for marketing," Pam notes. "Bonnie's email asked if we would be interested in helping. In order to have that conversation we needed to have a conversation. I wanted to see who these people were and have them see who we were, and make sure that there was a strong connection there."

Bonnie held her breath and clicked on the email as soon as it arrived.

"Come to Chicago. I want to meet you."

Oh my god. Oh my god. Oh my god.

Since there had to be a personal connection before any partnership could be discussed, let alone fleshed out, Pam did not come alone to our meeting. She brought two of her top people: MT Meadows, the head of professional practice, and the director of operations, Sue Gergely, who later become her chief operating officer. Partnerships were not something AONE gave away easily. Partners had to jump through the hoops of a value match, mission match, and vision match first. There had been a lot of talking at AONE, and everyone thought there was something very special about what we were trying to do. We appeared to be a match. In nursing terms, we had passed the clinical test. The meeting was to ensure our human side and the story we told were as genuine in person as they seemed on paper. We were now front and center with people who would decide whether we would come into their organization or not. Pam banked on MT and Sue seeing this, and thus everyone at AONE would see what she felt: that DAISY was a wonderful way to recognize nurses that had never been put before them. If we connected in person with each of them, the rest was just details.

It was clear we all felt a connection, and Pam was right about the details. And what details! The support we got from AONE from the relationship that started that day was more than we imagined. We became for all intents and purposes part of their family, and Pam made sure they provided what we needed to thrive as a member of that family. They invited us to be a part of the annual conference, not as a vendor but as a true partner. Our booth would not be in the exhibit hall but out front at registration so every attendee would see us—something AONE had never done before. They gave us their logo to put on our nomination forms and banners. They hired a half-time assistant for us in the Chicago office who would handle inquiries and follow up on them. AONE would also start building out our new database with us, which SalesForce had donated to DAISY as a qualifying nonprofit to manage our growing number of hospitals. That work alone would be life changing for us as a business.

Anything else that needed to be done, Pam said we would figure out as the relationship developed. "I'm not a rule-bound person," Pam explains. "When you're going after something that there's no pathway established for, you make it up as you go along. DAISY had been successful for so long, if this didn't work, we would just back away and say, 'What did I learn from this?'"

Mark liked everything he heard and had just one more question for Pam that he asked that night over a martini at dinner: "What happens if we come into in a disagreement in the future?"

"We just duke it out," Pam responded.

"That sealed it for me," Mark says. "I will remember that line for the rest of my life. We use it whenever we have a disagreement, 'Let's just duke it out.'"

That future, however, came sooner than anyone thought. Bonnie and Pam started duking it out before dessert.

Pam had one more thing on her mind. She looked at us across the table and bluntly addressed Bonnie's desire to keep giving DAISY as a gift: "Unless DAISY is a lot better off than it looks financially, this business model of yours has got to change. We're going to help you grow this program, but you won't be able to sustain it for long. We will bring the DAISY Award to many more hospitals than you could likely afford to fund. You have got to start charging for this program."

No one cares about nurses more than Pam, but by her own admission she can be a tough cookie. But Bonnie wasn't backing down . . . yet. "Pam, I can't do that," Bonnie said respectfully. "This is in memory of Our Patrick. I can't bring myself to do it. This is our gift to the nurses. I can't charge for it."

Bonnie looked at Pam's face as she spoke and knew immediately that if you wanted to do business with Pam, you don't say no to her without a really good business reason. And Bonnie didn't have one. Pam then politely explained why we were very wrong. She wasn't going into this recklessly. AONE's goal was to keep us running and growing long-term. She didn't have the expectation that we would stay dependent upon them. That wouldn't have been a good partnership. The value and impact DAISY provided were obviously significant. A fee would signify that value—putting their money where their mouths were, so to speak. We would bankrupt ourselves without that revenue.

"Nurse leaders will pay for the program," Pam stated confidently.

Mark was all in. He knew the value from our surveys the year before and now Pam echoed everything the hospitals said.

"Okay, we'll try," Bonnie conceded.

"Bonnie, they are going to pay for it. This is of great value. There's going to be no problem."

Bonnie wanted to believe but kept her thoughts to herself the rest of the evening. When we got home, she was still uncomfortable. She needed to be sure that Pam was right, and the only one way to do that was to talk to the chief nursing officers personally and ask them. So Bonnie called all 182 DAISY hospitals' chief nursing officers. And once again, not one of them said no. Not one thought the annual fee we agreed to with AONE—$1,250 for twelve awards per year—was unreasonable given the benefits DAISY was bringing their nurses. Every hospital went from promise to commitment as soon as the awards could be added to their budgets.

We instituted the fee in January 2008 along with our AONE partnership. That year we went from 182 to 317 hospitals. Those hospitals generated a big increase in expenses, but along with our sponsors and donors, not to mention our personal contributions, DAISY generated enough in income to cover it. We were not just going to survive as a business—we were going to thrive. AONE provided the guidance of nursing leadership to make our vision a sustainable reality. Pam Thompson believed the mark of our success would be that we could go and hire our own staff. That we then could go partner with as many other people and organizations as we wanted and grow it beyond our imagination.

We are often asked by other nursing organizations that support our mission why AONE (now AONL) gets to have their logo on our banner and honoree certificate. To us the reason is clear: They were the first. Their guidance was invaluable. We wouldn't be here without them. Pam saw what we were doing as universal, because nursing is universal. "You'll find that art, that essence, no matter where you find nurses," she says. "My privilege of meeting so many nurses internationally is that once you get down to that essence, all the other stuff doesn't matter. We have different governments, we have different health systems, but we all take care of patients and families. It's not about your technology. It's not about who or what has got the best systems. It has nothing to do with any of that. It's: Do you have nurses that understand how to deliver care at that level? That's what we do. That's what DAISY could help us do."

And we did. Because of AONE and Pam. Because of the *nurses*. All we wanted to do was thank you, and ten years later look what they did!

Everything DAISY was about to change for the better.

DAISY HONOREE STORY

Center for Psychiatry
Winter Haven Hospital
Winter Haven, FL

We have a patient who has been here on Center for Psychiatry (CFP) for over one month. She is a patient who came to us with a very traumatic background of abuse from facilities for years, per her mother. She can be very violent and when she first arrived would literally take down our nurses by the hair of the head to the floor. She trusted no one, not even her family. Since admission, our team has worked hard to develop a trusting relationship, provide a safe environment, and to build rapport with her. Staff discovered that if certain music is played the patient would sing along while they took care of her. The music kept the patient calm and distracted so the patient did not become violent. She showed joy when listening and singing to the music. The staff discovered her favorite foods and beverages to use as a tool to build trust and to get her to comply with taking her medications. They encouraged her to talk where they could get to know her, to build trust with her so she would know that she is safe here. We have two staff members with the patient at all times. Her family is afraid of her due to her violent, unpredictable behavior.

The mother came to visit recently and asked if it was safe to hug her daughter. We had four staff members at her side for safety just in case. The patient then looked at her mother and stated, "Mom, it is okay if you hug me. These people are not like all the others who hurt me. They are here to keep me safe. When I wake up and see them sitting at my side, I know that they are there to protect me from the voices and the bad people. So, Mom, I want you to come hug me and give me a kiss." The mother went over to her daughter and was able to hug and kiss her.

The mother cried, the staff cried, and it was a very special moment that reminded us why we do what we do here in Mental Health every day. The mother stated that this was the first place that her daughter has ever been [where] her daughter was treated with dignity, respect, and care. The mother stated that other places treated her daughter like a "wild animal" and never developed a relationship with her where she could make such a powerful statement.

This patient will continue to be unpredictable and dangerous, but the work that our staff has done with her is remarkable. The fact that the patient can actually use the words "They love me; they are here to protect me; I feel safe here; they don't hurt me like the others; when I wake up at night and see them there I know they are protecting me and most importantly, Mom, you can hug and kiss me; it's okay" speaks volumes about our staff here on CFP.

I am so proud to be the manager of CFP and these remarkable staff members. I cry every time I tell this story.

Growing DAISY
2008–2019

"The DAISY Award is very special because it is not about my degree or academic achievements. The award is about how I care for my patients and shows that my patient's family and my coworkers see how much I love to care for others."

Christine Duerksen, RN

What's a Nice Girl Like You . . .

audi Arabia, 2015. Bonnie was wandering the desert. Mark was sure of it. She had been gone 10 minutes in the pitch-black night surrounding their campsite in the vast sands surrounding Jeddah. Maybe in the story of Exodus, her people had wandered the desert for 40 years on their journey to the Promised Land. But Bonnie's a nice Jewish girl from New York City. She wasn't looking for the land of milk and honey, just the only tree nearby to pee behind. She had initially refused to go but necessity overcame her modesty. Mark pointed the way and out she went, iPhone with no cellular reception lighting the way. The tree wasn't far. Ten minutes was too long to be gone. So Mark stood outside the tent, called out for Bonnie, and a light suddenly appeared, a hundred yards away, headed in the wrong direction. She quickly turned around.

Ironically, Bonnie was only lost that night because by 2015 DAISY had been found and embraced by thousands of hospitals worldwide, including seven in Saudi Arabia (rising to 21 by our 20th anniversary). It's not lost on us that when we started DAISY we had been wandering too—maybe not in a desert but certainly unsure of exactly where we were going and how long it would take to get there. Not anymore. DAISY had started to cover the world like the sand that covered us the next morning after a sandstorm hit during the night.

How did we get here? Nurses, of course. Their compassionate care DAISY recognizes knows no borders.

Our 2015 trip wasn't our first to Saudi Arabia, though it was our first time camping there. Our hosts, King Faisal Specialist Hospital and Research Centre 's chief nursing officer Sandy Lovering and her husband, Craig, had piled us, tons of equipment, and extra tires into their Range Rover for a night. As we drove out of Jeddah, we don't know what fascinated us more: the baboons on the side of the road or the fact that there was a Cinnabon in the gas station we stopped at on the outskirts of the city. When we returned to Jeddah after a night at our magnificent campsite, we addressed the 7th International Nursing Symposium on Embracing Magnet in the Middle East.

Our first introduction to Saudi Arabia was in 2009 when we attended our first Magnet conference in the United States organized by the American Nurses Credentialing Center (ANCC). Magnet is the designation given by the ANCC to hospitals that excel in quality care delivered by nurses and their organizations. Earlier in the year, ANCC's executive director, Jeanne Floyd, had sent us a letter saying she had

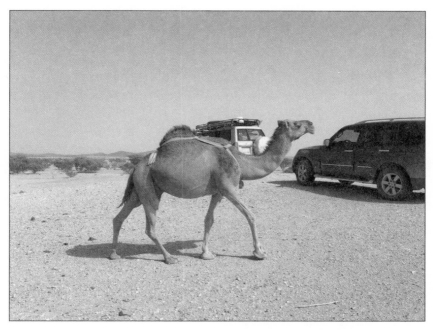

Camels and cars in the Saudi desert, 2015

become aware of our work. She hoped we would have time to talk with her about how ANCC could be helpful toward supporting the DAISY Award in every Magnet hospital—and eventually the organization's Pathway to Excellence program, which it was then in the process of acquiring. *Would we have time? Are you kidding us?* We were so excited you'd have thought DAISY had been designated Magnet!

To start, ANCC invited us to do what AONE did: set up our display outside the exhibit hall as a partner, not with the vendors. We put together a homemade booth, and that's where we were when we met Judy Moseley, who told us she'd like to bring DAISY to the hospital where she was chief nursing officer: King Faisal Specialist Hospital and Research Centre in Riyadh, Saudi Arabia. *You want to do what where?* Judy is a tall, blonde, stately woman who that day was dressed in a stylish, light pantsuit—hardly the match for what we pictured a Saudi nurse might look like. "I'm from Minneapolis," she explained, adding that most of the nurses at her hospital and throughout Saudi Arabia were expats. Nursing is not as respected a profession there as it is in the U.S. Judy wanted her staff to feel part of the global community of nurses and feel the pride of being honored with DAISY.

Our discussion with Judy tapped into our already growing excitement being at an international conference. We didn't know much about nursing in other countries, and our relationship with ANCC and presence at the Magnet conference was bound to bring even more international inquiries. This was all something new for us to consider as we grew. Thanks to our AONE relationship, DAISY was adding more than 100 hospitals a year and we projected close to 500 total by the end of 2009. But we had only one international hospital and it wasn't all that foreign: The Hospital for Sick Children in Toronto. Bonnie had been thinking about approaching one of the nursing organizations in Canada to do what AONE had done for us here. But did we want to expand overseas? Serving Canada didn't seem like it should be that much harder or different from serving the States.

Was DAISY just about American nursing? Would honoring nurses internationally distract us from our growth at home—growth we had just started to manage now that hospitals were paying?

In the end, we decided DAISY was about honoring the compassionate care of nurses anywhere they are, and King Faisal Specialist Hospital and Research Centre in Riyadh became our first hospital outside of North America, quickly followed by King Faisal in Jeddah and the American University Medical Center in Beirut. By the end of 2010, we had six international partners. But it wasn't until 2012 when Donna Hilliard, director of nursing education at King Fahad Medical City in Riyadh, invited us to speak at an international nursing symposium that we understood firsthand the global connection between nurses and DAISY—and that nurses are nurses everywhere.

Getting to talk to nurses in Saudi Arabia was a big deal! To meet those nurses in Saudi Arabia, however, Bonnie needed to dress appropriately. Our friend and DAISY Nurse Deidre Stewart bought her a long black abaya so she would be covered neck to toe and a chiffon *shayla* (scarf) to cover her hair (she was not required to cover half her face with a veil). She put them on before we landed in Riyadh and even found the abaya really comfortable when she wasn't tripping on its length. As a man, Mark had no such restrictions on his dress but would happily have dressed any way they wanted for a glass of wine with dinner; the Saudi ban on alcohol had started on the plane.

Donna greeted us at the airport wearing a lab coat and a shayla similar to Bonnie's, her outfit almost the entire time we were with her. After 18 years in Saudi Arabia, Donna and many of the other expat nurses were adept at navigating and explaining the "Saudi way." When we spotted all the logos of American fast-food chains on our drive from the hotel—McDonald's, KFC, Taco Bell, the names all written in Arabic—Donna told us the country didn't have an obesity problem until those chains came to town. When we spotted several Starbucks, Donna told us women are not welcome to sit in the same area as men. In the hospital, she showed us separate waiting and prayer rooms for men only. How do female nurses treat patients of the opposite sex? More jarring was seeing all the Saudi women—nurses and patients—in

Nurses welcoming us at King Faisal Specialist Hospital and Research Centre
Jeddah, 2015

the hospital dressed in abayas and shaylas with black veils that left only their eyes showing. How do they deal with the abayas for IVs?

We had all our questions answered, because underneath the dress the nurses were the same welcoming, informative, gracious, proud, and of course compassionate people we knew in the States. They talked with us about the clinical and compassionate challenges of being a nurse in Saudi Arabia. We are told that families are obligated by Islam to visit their patients, and as many as 15 people might be in a room at any time. Sometimes they bring in food and lay it out on blankets on the floor. The nurses have a tough time dealing with this just to control infection, but family and spiritual requirements are heeded first and foremost. Because that's where compassion has its origin in an Islamic hospital, and they put the needs of the patient first. Donna and her colleagues told us they hoped DAISY would soon come to King Fahad Medical City.

We would soon know how likely that was, because before we spoke at the conference, the hospital's chief nursing officer, Jane Wilshaw, had arranged for a meeting with King Fahad Medical City's CEO, Abdullah Al Amro. Jane had shared the abstract of our talk with him ("The Power of Gratitude: Driving Patient- and Family-Centered Care with Nurse Recognition"), and he asked to meet with us and the nurses to discuss DAISY. While waiting in his sitting room outside his office, two men in black suits brought us dates and cardamom coffee, and we realized we did not know what to expect. We had been given very specific instructions from dress to decorum, like don't touch him unless he reaches out to you. We did not know if Bonnie would be permitted to speak. The nurses around us fidgeted nervously.

As soon as we were ushered in, a tall, slender, bearded man wearing the traditional Arabic dress we had only seen on sheiks in pictures and on TV greeted us. He sat in a big chair and motioned at the sofa next to him for us to sit. He leaned in and said, "Tell me your story." With those words, Dr. Al Amro completely disarmed us and listened intently as we told him the story of DAISY. He told us his story too, covering his training in Canada, his family, his work as a doctor, his recent recognition as CEO of the year, his upcoming trip to Korea to speak, and his eagerness to step down from his marathon job. He then told us he had great regard for nurses and was totally supportive of DAISY being part of King Fahad Medical City. He was excited to kick off the program with us.

We spent 20 minutes together before we headed down to the auditorium to speak. Dr. Al Amro gave the opening speech on the history of nursing in the Arab world, going all the way back to Maimonides. He then invited us on stage to receive a gift from him. Bonnie still didn't know whether to shake his hand or not. (When Bonnie got on the elevator to head to the auditorium, the men backed away from her.) But he immediately put his hand out to shake hers. Much to Mark's chagrin, Bonnie still has a crush on him.

Our meetings with the nurses and Dr. Al Amro showed us the universal power of recognition and gratitude. Even in a country where nurses did not command universal respect, and regardless of any cultural differences between our countries, DAISY has been warmly welcomed. Today, our signs are in Arabic and numerous other languages including Mandarin (although our daisy in China is red, as white is the color of death). We have circled the globe several times over to visit many of the countries DAISY is in and have been greeted in ways we will never forget. In São Paulo, Brazil, nurses at the Hospital Israelita Albert Einstein seemed to take every daisy in South America to create a floor-to-ceiling curtain of daisies as a backdrop for our visit. At Bumrungrad International Hospital in Bangkok, we were shown by the CEO how every DAISY Nurse receives a gorgeous banner with their nomination story written on it. At Nottingham University Hospitals NHS Trust in England, the nurse leaders had a DAISY tea for us dressed up in vintage nursing outfits, displaying the history of their uniforms through the years. The tables were set with their personal tea sets. The chief nurse at England's Northampton General Hospital even goes on local radio asking for patients to nominate nurses.

And then there is Vietnam. We are there because of one man: Greg Crow, a nurse who tragically passed away in 2019. Greg had

Riley Barnes Carraher and Peter Maher joined Bonnie and Mark at the dedication of the DAISY Wall at Nottingham University Hospitals NHS Trust in England, 2018. The nurses dressed in vintage nursing outfits.

been a professor at the University of San Francisco and had become a consultant to hospitals on shared governance. We heard him speak at an event at San Francisco General Hospital where he was given its Friend of Nursing Award, an honor DAISY had received a year earlier. Greg detailed his volunteer work in Vietnam, a country he loved. He described how he educated nurses through a program called the Vietnam Nurses Project, in which he took nurse educators from San Francisco and beyond to work with the Vietnamese nurses on clinical care. We met him briefly after the event and asked if he knew about the DAISY Award. He did and told us that he would love to bring it to Vietnam. Sure enough, a couple of years later he called and said, "I'm going to Vietnam, and I'm bringing DAISY with me. Do you want to come?" We shipped a big box of everything needed and tagged along with him for the first DAISY ceremony.

When we say nurses are nurses everywhere in the world, this trip exemplified it. It doesn't matter how broad or limited their scope of practice is. They still have that human heart that beats at the center of DAISY and owns the program no matter what language they speak. But we had never seen conditions like the ones in the first hospital we visited in Vietnam. Their intensive care unit was a twelve-bed ward. There were no individual rooms. Family members helped patients in the ICU. There was a washing machine in the back and sheets hanging by the windows to dry. The nurses in Saudi Arabia had every resource imaginable. The nurses here lacked basic items like stethoscopes, and seemed pleased to have running water. (The government hospital we visited later that trip had the best of the best, but not this one.) And yet the nurses there were just as heartbreakingly wonderful, conscientious, and compassionate as those in Saudi Arabia and in the most modern and technologically advanced hospitals in the United States we knew. Part of the goal of the Vietnam Nurses Project would be to use DAISY to upgrade the level of acceptance and recognition of nurses in the country.

As of 2019, DAISY honors nurses in more than 150 hospitals in 25 countries outside the United States. In addition to our work with the American Nurses Credentialing Center, our partnerships with the International Council of Nursing and Sigma Theta Tau International help us reach nurses worldwide.

But we have gotten ahead of ourselves in this story, because while we have done most of the international visits, we no longer oversee the international hospitals day-to-day. They are served at DAISY by a woman who joined us in 2011 and was used to opening a Starbucks store she managed at 3:00 A.M.—and thus never minds being up early to do international webinars: Melissa Barnes, one of our daughters-in-law. In our second decade, DAISY had become a family business, starting with the person who shared the memory of Our Patrick with us the most.

DAISY HONOREE STORY

Jisha George, RN
King Faisal Specialist Hospital and Research Centre
Jeddah, Saudi Arabia

I would like to thank all the general pediatric staff nurses for their good manner and very hard work and especially the nurses who really made a difference to us as patients and sitters.

My daughter was admitted to general pediatric floor during my college examinations time, so I asked my sister to stay with my daughter while I [went] home to study for my next-day exam. Suddenly, during the nighttime, my sister got sick when she had dizziness, tachycardia, shortness of breath, and numbness.

My sister called me but since my home is so far away from hospital, I asked her to call any nurse for help. She opened the room door and found Ms. Jisha, who offered her help, checked her vital signs, then accompanied her to the emergency room and kept checking on her till I arrived. At the same time, Ms. Jisha went back quickly to the room and took care of my sick daughter who was alone that time, she stayed with her, reassured her, and cuddled her in addition to her regular medical/nursing care.

Honestly, I want Ms. Jisha to know how much I appreciate her kindness, dedication, consideration, and cooperation to take care of my sick sister and sick daughter. Not to mention her professional attitude, hard work, good manners, kind heart, and big warm smile.

"I cannot tell you how incredibly special this DAISY Award has been to me. It may sound crazy but having received this award has made me a better nurse. The sense of pride that I feel when people that I barely know come up to congratulate me and tell me that no one deserves it more, it brings tears to my eyes each time."

Donna Young, RN

We Are Family

"How are you going to manage three young kids and do school full time?"

Tena looked at Bonnie, tears welling in her eyes as she answered. "I don't know and quite frankly I'm terrified."

It was just before Christmas of 2009, and we were visiting Tena and Riley in Atlanta for the holiday and Tena's birthday. Bonnie and Tena were doing the dishes while the rest of the family made noise in the dining room. Tena had remarried in the years after Patrick died, to a lovely man named John Carraher, and they'd had two children together, Lauren and Kate. She had been raising all three kids while we were raising DAISY. She was also working for the advertising company where she and Patrick had met in Atlanta. But now Tena wanted to build a new career as . . . a nurse! She had been accepted at a local nursing college and was to start after the holidays.

Tena's decision to become a nurse wasn't entirely because of DAISY. She was not involved in our day-to-day operations, though she had been on our board from the beginning and attended every meeting. She went to local DAISY events too, and had even introduced the awards to Piedmont Hospital in downtown Atlanta after Lauren was born and had to spend some time in the NICU. Initially being involved in anything public for DAISY was difficult for Tena. She loved John deeply, but the memory of losing Patrick still made her emotional. We saw this firsthand when we came in for the inaugural DAISY Award at Piedmont. "As I stepped forward to present I thought, *I've got this. I can do this*," Tena recalls. "I think I squeaked out three words and the tears came and I just took a couple steps back. Mark and Bonnie stepped forward and I said, 'Okay, maybe I'm not ready to be on my own yet.'"

Since then, Tena has learned to "turn her feelings upside down" for the most part and smiles at all that DAISY is doing in Pat's memory, remembering their happy times together and focusing on the nurses. And of course there was Riley. DAISY connected Riley to the memory of the father she never got to know. Tena brought her to every board meeting, and she attended other events, too. It wasn't *that* hard to get her to go. Like father, like daughter: Riley would go anywhere for a Cinnabon. But she also loved the nurses, and the nurses loved when she came to events with Tena or us, especially when we visited Riley Children's Hospital in Indiana. In 2011, Riley participated in the 10th anniversary celebration of our first award at the University of Washington. In 2012, she asked to go on our three-week drive to visit hospitals in the Midwest.

But it wasn't Riley's or her connection to DAISY that pushed Tena to want a career in nursing. It was a nurse she met at Piedmont who told her she had lost her son to leukemia at age nine. "I decided to be a nurse to give back to the nurses who took care of him." Tena thought, *This is what I want to do. I've met so many nurses who have made such a difference and this could be a way that I can give back.* So she went back to school to do the math and science prerequisites she needed in addition to her bachelor's degree, and she was finally ready to start nursing school in January 2010. But just taking the time to complete those prerequisites had been stressful. Tena said her family was "pretty much on strike because all I did was study or go to class." Bonnie knew this, which was why she asked the question about how she would manage.

Not because we wanted to pry, but because we had another question ready.

"This is probably bad timing, but we're growing," Bonnie said. "We really need someone to work full-time for the foundation. Why don't you come work for DAISY and not go to nursing school?"

Tena looked at Bonnie and asked wryly, "Why didn't you discuss this with me two years ago when I was starting my prerequisites?!"

"Because we didn't know we would need you," Bonnie replied. DAISY was now adding well over 200 hospitals a year and projected to reach 1,000 hospitals by 2012. One part-time person from AONE was not nearly enough to get the work done. "I'm drowning and need help."

Our vision was Tena would be the point of contact in the East, Bonnie in the West, and Mark would handle the finances and shipping with the help of John Reynolds. Tena said she needed to talk to her husband and think about it. She promised an answer before we left. We understood why and did not take it personally. She had worked hard to get into nursing school and had been looking forward to becoming a nurse. But she soon realized DAISY was her first labor of love, and the possibility of honoring so many nurses would allow her to impact more people than she ever imagined.

Tena accepted our job offer two days later, and we all started hugging and crying. That's when Lauren came in and said, "Mommy, does this mean that you're a nurse now?"

"No," Tena answered, "but I'm going to be working with nurses."

"Okay."

And then Lauren joined the hugging and crying as well.

⚜ ⚜ ⚜

Truth be told, we needed Tena for more than just the work. We needed someone who understood DAISY. Who felt a connection to it and the nurses. Who understood its mission. Who would love it. No one could have a closer connection to the origin story of DAISY than she did, but she also understood why DAISY was different from any other recognition program. She got the importance of it not coming from within the hospital. Plus her desire to be a nurse gave her added respect for them and their ability to manage work, life, continuing education, and family and be as she says "multitasking, high achieving, amazing humans."

"I hear a lot of nurses say, 'DAISY came when I needed it the most' or 'This award made me feel like I made a difference' or 'It means so much that someone took the time to do this for me.'" Tena says. "In this day and age, I think a lot of people will take the time to write a complaint. We wanted patients and families to tell their stories and thank their nurses for making a positive impact. I think that so many people do it speaks volumes about the profession and for DAISY as well. When we're visiting hospitals or at conferences, nurses come up and want to personally thank us. They want to hug us, take pictures with us. They cry when they explain what it meant to them to be nominated for and receive the DAISY Award. One nurse came up to me and said she had been a nurse for 52 years and pointed at her nominee pin. 'This was from a patient. It was one of the highlights of my career.' She just wanted to say thank you to us, but our mission was to say thank you to people like her. And now they 'owned' the program!"

Tena got it for sure, but with DAISY growing so rapidly we soon needed more help—a lot more help. Mark could not possibly handle the finances, order everything that went with the awards, and do most of the shipping, along with everything else he was doing. Bonnie needed more than just Tena to support the organizational work. We needed someone who understood standardization *and* that everything we do is about supporting the nurses, helping them execute the program, and educating them on how to take best advantage of it. We needed another person who would love DAISY.

Lucky for us, we had another daughter-in-law who was expert in all that we needed to help transform DAISY operationally: Auntie Bonkers.

Auntie Bonkers is Riley's nickname for Melissa Barnes, Patrick's brother Adam's wife, who lives in Seattle. The nickname belies her professional skill but not her personality. In 2011, Melissa was managing a large and successful Starbucks. We were having breakfast with her one morning and started pumping her for information on how Starbucks makes sure everything is done the same way and remains true to the values of the brand. She knew why we were asking and shifted the conversation to us and DAISY and what we could be doing.

The two of us had the same thought: *Melissa should be working for DAISY.* "What are you doing at Starbucks? You should be working for DAISY! You can see your kids in the morning. If you come work for us, you can have a life!"

Melissa smiled, "I've been hoping you would ask me."

We knew Melissa, like Tena, would succeed not just because she was smart and a good worker but because she also loved DAISY and the nurses we served. "Having married Patrick's brother and seeing what Bonnie and Mark were doing—the excitement whenever they made a partnership with a new hospital. Watching it grow and grow and grow and seeing everything they got to do. . . . They got to share gratitude with nurses. I don't think you're going to find very many people that say, 'I get to work for my in-laws and enjoy it.' It was the perfect job for me," Melissa recalls.

At first Melissa took over the western United States from Bonnie in 2011 and then dove into our systems. We had a plan for communicating with hospitals, and we had SalesForce up and running fairly well. We were handling billing and shipping. We had a "welcome kit" for every new hospital we signed up that included a binder explaining chapter and verse of how to run the program. The problem was, we were not as systematic as we wanted to be. DAISY didn't feel scalable. Melissa's operational skills and experience were perfect for us. She would set up the standards that would make us better at serving our "customers" as we continued to grow.

Melissa's goal was to continually find what worked really well, get feedback from us and Tena on what we needed, and then take that and figure out a way to share it with everyone who had the program. To do this, she took the time to understand why some programs got so much out of DAISY, and she used that to create a set of best practices that we shared with all the hospitals via webinars. She used her business and buying background to create an operations plan so every new organization was trained on how to implement DAISY from the moment they signed up. Everything our partners needed to do to be successful was included, and they were trained in how to do it all: building a selection committee, attracting nominations, tracking and blinding nominations, building awareness with marketing and PR, using the materials and templates we provided for nomination forms and award certificates, scheduling and presenting awards, and ordering more.

Tena worked with Melissa to revamp our welcome kit and connect it more effectively to a new password-protected Resource Center on our website. Melissa then worked with all of us to adapt SalesForce into what we needed to capture everything from communications history to stories. To handle all this, Melissa used her human resources experience to hire her own team, initially a few people she had managed at Starbucks, growing to DAISY's current team of 15 based in their home offices all over the United States. And when we put more energy behind our international growth, Melissa's comfort getting up in the middle of the night to open her Starbucks store, combined with her interest in foreign culture, made her an easy fit to oversee DAISY's growing international footprint, too.

With Tena, Melissa, and our growing regional staff on board, we started to see how we could step back from the day-to-day work as

Ten years later we're still family: Melissa, Tena, Bonnie, and Mark, 2019.
Photo by Kenneth Krehbiel, Imageworks Photography.

the organization grew, focusing our efforts on strategic planning and DAISY's visibility to the nursing profession. They gave us the expertise and bandwidth to ensure that DAISY delivered on our commitment to the nurses and hospitals since the liquid dinner: that the program would be turnkey. We would guide its implementation with the hospitals, and they could customize it to their size and culture.

But most importantly with Tena and Melissa, we had and were building a staff that feels like our family. Mark was finally getting what he wanted: DAISY was running like a family *and* a business. Everyone knew that Our Patrick was the reason DAISY existed and that everything reminded nurses how special they are. Melissa's systems were making everything run more efficiently. In other words, our standards reflected the equivalent of compassionate care and clinical excellence— the standards nurses hold themselves to every day.

Our board, now filled with chief nursing officers and leaders in the healthcare industry, ensured this as well, as did the man who would become our chief financial officer, Peter Maher. Peter came from Mark's second family: the advertising business he had sold years before DAISY. Peter had risen from staff accountant to chief financial officer under Mark, and there was no one Mark trusted more with money. Peter had left the business shortly after Mark did and started his own financial consulting company. So when DAISY was growing, Mark constantly called him with accounting questions. Peter soon started volunteering his time doing what he called the "bits and pieces" to help us, refusing to take any money. But what started with him setting up a simple accounting system soon became more complex work. More than half of Peter's consulting work is now for DAISY, so we offered and he begrudgingly accepted a small pittance for his time. In 2010, we asked Peter to join our board and assume the title of chief financial officer, which he has been ever since.

But Peter's love for DAISY is not because of his close friendship to Mark. Given the opportunity, Mark will tell the tale of Peter proving his disloyalty to him when he happened to be in attendance for one of our aggressive discussions. As Mark recalls, Peter immediately took Bonnie's side: "This was a man I had placed all my trust in. A man I personally raised through the ranks of my previous company, as well as DAISY. And then when an opportunity to support me in my hour of need presented itself, he chose to rush to the other side. I now call him by one name: Benedict." Ah, family.

What binds ~~Benedict~~ Peter to DAISY is what binds us all: the nurses. Peter has made exactly one demand of us since he started: to attend the annual Magnet Conference with us so he can be with the nurses. He hangs out at our booth and talks to nurses. He takes pictures with them. He takes pictures of us with them. He asks them to tell their stories. He thanks them. You see, Peter had open heart surgery in 2009 after other procedures failed to make him better. (He was only in his forties but has a family history of heart disease.) He never forgot what the nurses meant to him during the entire process, and the comfort they gave him as he recovered.

Because everyone has a nurse story, and to serve those nurses and their stories, the DAISY Awards were about to expand their reach.

DAISY HONOREE STORY

Dana Mantundan, RN

Mercy Hospital South

St. Louis, Missouri

My mom told many stories of Dana and what a sweet soul she is. I know that it takes a very special person to become a nurse, but Dana was caring, kind, and sweet beyond words.

Dana was one of my mom's nurses during her final time on earth. My mom had Stage 4 lung cancer and the cancer had spread all over her body. Dana made friends with my mom right away. On many occasions, Dana would make my mom cookies and bring some to her. Some of her favorites were red velvet and snickerdoodles.

On one evening, Dana even painted my mom's toenails while they chatted at 3:00 A.M. These things were unbelievable. I witnessed their sweet friendship on a few occasions, and it made my heart smile. She was always kind. One particular evening, I left the room and when I came back my mom's bed was covered in a beautiful teal and light blue paisley sheet that matched her eyes. She was beaming in happiness as she told me about it. Next to her was Nurse Dana holding a bag of coconut candy—all kinds. You see, coconut was my mom's favorite. It didn't matter if it was a cake, cookie, pie, donuts or candy; she just loved coconut.

As Dana walked out of the room, I followed her. I gave her a huge hug and thanked her for loving my mom. She said that she never had a patient like my mom. She was a breath of fresh air and others in her situation did not have the attitude that she had.

Dana is an excellent nurse, she encompasses what we all should be more like. Thank you again, Dana. Mom adored you, too. Please know you made her last days here happier!

"Being a DAISY Team Award winner is such a humbling experience. This award recognized all our team for a job well done. I'm so proud of all of our nurses and the true difference they make each and every day!"

Meredith Hartzog, BSN, RN, CVRN-BC

What Happened to Turnkey?!

When we conceived of the DAISY Awards, one of our objectives was to create a turnkey operation. And it was. It consisted of an award pin, a certificate in a Costco frame (later a professional portfolio), a box of Cinnabons, a massage, dinner, and (a year into the program) the *Healer's Touch* sculpture. Very simple. Very turnkey. Then, as Mark says, "Nurses really screwed that up."

First came their inspiration for the addition of a banner. *That's terrific, let's steal, um, share that idea with everyone else.* Then came a nominee pin. *Love that—let's make them for everyone!* Then they opened our eyes to the fact that the massage and dinner were unimportant—that DAISY is about the recognition. *Wonderful, we don't want to give nurses something that isn't important to them!* How about that great DAISY Committee button: ASK ME ABOUT THE DAISY AWARD? *We need that, too! Let's order them.* Then the multiple nominee pin. *Really?! Another great addition!*

Every time we caught up to nurses' ideas, they came up with a new one. In other words, nurses kept making the DAISY Awards better. But if we thought nurses would stop there, we were sadly mistaken. They then made the DAISY Awards bigger, not just better.

Actually, the first time a nurse caused us to expand DAISY wasn't for the awards but for the foundation itself, and connected to one of our ideas from the liquid dinner in 1999 with Tena and Dianne that started it all: funding research in treatment of patients with autoimmune diseases like ITP. We had given up the research dream once we realized we didn't have the money to make a difference. But even as we grew, we wanted research to be part of the DAISY mission somehow. We mentioned this at the 2007 DAISY board meeting, hoping our advisors would have thoughts on how we could raise funds for it and where the money might go.

Cindy Angiulo, assistant administrator for the University of Washington Medical Center who had made it her charge to put our first DAISY Awards together in 2001, had an idea. "If you are so interested in research," she said, looking around the table, "then why not marry your passion for nurses' care for patients with your desire to fund research for patient care by starting a grant program for nursing research?"

We'll be candid: When Cindy proposed this, we were stunned. We looked at each other, and Bonnie blurted out what Mark was also thinking, "Nurses do *research*?"

We had no idea of the level of science being applied by nurses to patient care through thoughtful, structured research studies. And we didn't really understand what evidence-based practice projects were or how they differed from research studies. It was a huge epiphany and suffice it to say, Cindy and the other nurses on the board gave us a thorough education. When they were done, we had the foundation for the launch of the J. Patrick Barnes Grants for Nursing Research and Evidence-Based Practice Projects.

Since Patrick had cancer as a young man and then ITP, we decided to focus on providing grants for nursing research and evidence-based projects designed to improve care for patients with one of those two conditions. To ensure the projects connected to DAISY's dedication to nurses and their direct care of patients, we made one of the requirements that staff nurses have to be deeply engaged in every study. For example, if a proposal involved surveys, nurse-researchers needed to have staff nurses analyze those surveys, not simply hand them out and log the answers. By nurturing this culture of inquiry among nurses, DAISY would also play a role in ensuring patients stayed at the heart of evidence-based healthcare.

Cindy agreed to chair the program and asked Elizabeth Bridges, a world-renowned researcher and critical care nurse, to build a volunteer panel of nurse-scientists to review applications. Liz loved the idea, especially about engaging staff nurses in research. The DAISY grant program just took off from there. By 2019, we had committed approximately $500,000 to hundreds of nurses' projects. Today, the program is run by a panel of 13 nurse-scientists. The panelists make sure that the projects we fund are well thought out and good science. To help our grantees disseminate their findings throughout the world of patient care, we added the Lynne Doll Grants for Dissemination of Findings in memory of our dear, departed board member and friend. Those grants provide funding for nurses to present their work at nursing conferences, and can be used for things like poster production, conference fees, and travel. In addition, in 2019, after we kept getting calls from nurses about asking for funding for the medical missions they were going on, we added the DAISY Medical Mission Grants, for DAISY to help pay for their participation in missions that allow them to share their compassion and skill with nurses and patients in underserved areas.

Shining the Light on All the Right

✿ ✿ ✿

With the grant program now in place, nurses turned their attention to the reach and mission of the awards themselves and whom they went to, because more nurses than we ever imagined wanted to be DAISY Nurses. Consider these words a nurse manager said to us during her hospital's award celebration: "I love DAISY and that my nurses are getting this kind of recognition. They really deserve it for all they do at the bedside. But I'll never be a DAISY! I'm not eligible because I'm not doing much direct care anymore."

We're not identifying that nurse by name, because she was not unique. In talking to nurse managers and directors, we heard a similar refrain and took it to heart. In addition, more and more organizations wanted to recognize their nurse leaders in a meaningful way. After all, nurse leaders have a tremendous impact on patient care and the environments where the compassion DAISY recognizes is going on. We wouldn't have had great nurses at Patrick's bedside if they hadn't had leaders empowering and supporting them. And many nurse leaders do hands-on work with patients.

So we created the DAISY Nurse Leader Award to express gratitude for courageous and caring nurse leaders who inspire compassion and create environments in which it can thrive. Nurse leaders who listen. Who help their nurses find the extraordinary in everyday acts of kindness. Who recognize the power nurses have to touch others. We launched the DAISY Nurse Leader Award at the 2015 AONE Annual Meeting and recognized the first recipients later that year. Over time, participating DAISY organizations have used this award to recognize lots of nursing roles such as preceptors, educators, charge nurses, and informaticists who have an indirect impact on patient care.

Okay, fine, the DAISY Nurse Leader Award was the one new award that we initiated, but it was still inspired by nurses who compelled us to screw up our turnkey operation ourselves. Not so the DAISY Team Award, which had arrived a couple of years before.

✿ ✿ ✿

Of course, celebrating teamwork was one of the reasons that we asked that Patrick's gift to his nurses—Cinnabon cinnamon rolls—be shared with everyone in the DAISY Honorees' units. Because that's what Patrick wanted when we brought him Cinnabons in the hospital. DAISY Nurses constantly reminded us that they could not do what they do without their teams. But it took a phone call in 2013 from Rachel Behrendt, a nurse leader and at the time our key contact at Thomas Jefferson University Hospital in Philadelphia, to get us to add teams to the DAISY Award roster. She told us about all the DAISY Award nominations Thomas Jefferson was receiving for teams doing extraordinary things for patients and their families who couldn't name a specific person who did something more spectacular than another.

DAISY Team Award to the Surgical Care Unit at Children's National Medical Center, Washington, DC, 2017

"I need to create a team award. How would you feel about a team award?" she asked.

"Are the teams made up of all nurses?"

"Not always."

"Are they nurse led?"

"Yes. Always."

"Then let's do it."

Thus the DAISY Team Award was created with Rachel piloting the first one. And we are so glad it was. It has been a great addition to our statement of gratitude to nurses. Over the years we have heard many Team Award stories about baptisms, graduations, weddings, special outings, end-of-life celebrations . . . But none touched us more than when we presented the award to the nurses and staff at Adventist Feather River Hospital in Paradise, California.

Paradise is the town that was destroyed in the horrific Camp Fire of 2018. As the town burned, more than 40 Adventist Health Feather River nurses and staff remained to evacuate the hospital. *As their own homes were on fire and they were thinking they would never see their families again, their first duty was to their patients.* Think about that. For a time, these people did not think they would survive, let alone be able to help their patients. Yet these heroes managed to evacuate 62 patients—some just out of surgery, some just born—in 45 minutes. We had the privilege of personally presenting the DAISY Team Award to them in 2018, and it was among the most moving moments in our entire DAISY journey. Their stories were harrowing, their courage and strength impossible to fully capture in words and almost unbelievable. It was truly a miracle they all survived and can tell their chilling stories today. (You can watch a video that captures some of those stories on YouTube. Just search for "Angels in Paradise.")

The near-instant acceptance of the DAISY Team Award by the nurses was no doubt also due, in part, to the increased emphasis in healthcare on building interprofessional teams. As a result, it allowed doctors—who are also not eligible for DAISY Awards but often long to be—to be recognized as part of the teams they value being a part of. One chief of staff at a hospital was so eager to be recognized by DAISY, he kept poking his head into our event there, filling our water glasses, and asking us if doing this would allow us to "make him a DAISY." We told him that's not how it works, but if he was on a nurse-led team, then he would get the recognition he longed for along with the nurses and staff.

Mary Dee Hacker, formerly the chief nursing officer at Children's Hospital Los Angeles and a member of our board, sums up the power of the Team Award perfectly: "DAISY Nurses love being DAISY Nurses. The Team Award is a cherished and appreciated recognition that extends DAISY's reach. It's amazing to me to see that people who are the most excited about receiving the award are the physicians who love the feeling of recognition and gratitude. Like the nurses, they choose their profession for a lot of reasons but primarily because they want to make a difference. They want to do something that matters. So much of the environment in healthcare is about productivity standards and outcome measurements. To pause for a few minutes and hear someone say, 'We want to thank you for your heart' really matters."

The irony is that the emphasis in healthcare on interprofessional teams is the number one reason some hospitals do not have the DAISY Awards at all: Some don't want to honor nurses separately. They think it undermines morale to have a recognition program that focuses on nurses as a separate entity and want to have the same award for all their disciplines. Okay, but in the end a single standardized recognition program for all employees could never do what DAISY does for nurses. Nurses have a unique connection to a hospital's customers: the patients. It's the individualized and personalized approach of DAISY to deliver meaningful recognition to those nurses from patients and other nurses that makes it so important to them—and by extension the culture and morale of the hospital as a whole. In fact, when one hospital group that did not have the DAISY Award bought a hospital that did and then told the hospital to drop DAISY, they refused. But it also showed that organizations can change. Not only does the hospital that was acquired still have DAISY, but all but one in the system that bought it have added DAISY.

Not that we think DAISY is or will ever be for everybody. We know DAISY cannot honor everyone and thus have chosen not to be for everyone. For example, we heard certified nursing assistants and nursing techs were feeling left out of DAISY, and over the years we have gotten a lot of pressure either to include them as part of the awards or to create an award for them. These are very compassionate people no doubt and do provide hands-on care. But they are not nurses, and we decided not to change. We had to put a stake in the ground and say DAISY is for professional nurses. Our experience when Patrick was hospitalized was with nurses. Not CNAs or respiratory therapists or anyone else. It was Pat's nurses who inspired us to say thank you. If an organization wanted to recognize nursing assistants and nursing techs or other nonlicensed staff, then just like doctors they could be part of the Team Award. If an organization still wanted separate awards for different staff, they can create one. We are happy to share our model with anyone who asks—and we have! We helped a friend create the PHIL Award for outstanding respiratory therapists. And we salute all the awards hospitals have created to provide recognition to nonnursing employees who demonstrate compassion and dedication to patients.

That said, Mark created something to show gratitude for people who do something wonderful for us: the DAISY Founders' Coin. He loved the idea of the coin traditionally given in the military as a way for senior leaders to show their appreciation in a more tangible way than a spoken thank you. Our DAISY Founders' Coin says those words in writing: Our DAISY daisy on the front and just a simple THANK YOU on the back. Everyone we give them to is blown away by the gesture. The coins are also heavy and feel almost indestructible, because as Mark says, "A thank-you is indestructible."

But let's get back to the nurses screwing up our turnkey operations. Next up was a hospital and their nurses that wanted to recognize their DAISY Coordinator. She was doing all the work for the program, like the arduous job of clearing the calendars of the hospital's leadership to be available when the nurse was being honored, blinding nominations (sometimes more than 100 a month), and getting the cinnamon rolls. She tended to the myriad details her committee came up with to make their award presentations so special. So we introduced the DAISY Champion. These champions are sometimes—but not always—administrative assistants or unit clerks who go above and beyond to make their DAISY programs the best they can be. The presentation allows *them* for once to be the ones who get to sit back and relish what it feels like to receive the recognition that they have made happen for so many nurses. Every champion gets a personal video message from Bonnie, and she has recorded hundreds of them. We get videos of the presentations to DAISY Champions, and we never tire of watching them.

Next up was the DAISY Faculty Award, which came out of a discussion with the board, which you might recall is made up of mostly nurses—nurses who clearly remain in cahoots with those screwing up our turnkey operations from outside the organization. In this case it was Beth Heyman, formerly of the Health Alliance of Greater Cincinnati and now dean of the Galen College of Nursing in Cincinnati, who said, "You know, somebody had to teach those nurses who took care of Patrick." Holy smokes! This was a real slap-in-the-forehead moment for us, considering our first award was delivered at a university hospital.

We'll be honest, though: As obvious as the idea was, this award did not take off the way the Nurse Leader and Team Awards would when they were introduced. We just couldn't get schools to accept it. The vast majority of deans we cold-called were not interested in recognition like this. They told us that for faculty, recognition was about presentations, publications, and tenure. As a result, we had fewer than 100 colleges of nursing after five years.

That all changed in May 2018 when we were traveling through Michigan during Nurse's Week. One of our stops was at the University of Michigan's nursing school, which had the faculty award program. We asked Dean Patty Hurn if we could meet their honorees, and she brought a bunch of them in to talk about what the DAISY Faculty Award meant to them. What one of them said impacted us deeply: "I was getting ready to retire and this award bought me five more years of teaching. When my students stood up and applauded for me when I was recognized with this DAISY Award, it meant the world to me." We knew right then we needed to invest a lot more energy into this program. We were acutely aware there was a real shortage of nursing faculty, because a lot of teachers were retiring. Faculty who remain in the hospitals and classrooms are on total overload. DAISY couldn't solve that, but it was clearly having some impact.

We asked Dean Hurn if she thought the American Association of Colleges of Nursing (AACN) would be the right organization to issue a national call to action for nursing faculty recognition. We had been collaborating with AACN since we started the Faculty Award, but growth had been really slow. Maybe if they heard why the DAISY Faculty Award had been so important to her, her faculty, and others we would ask to join us in this venture, we could get on AACN's agenda for their fall meeting. We would also approach Susan Groenwald to join us on our call with AACN. Susan was the president of Chamberlain University, a for-profit healthcare and nursing school that had campuses nationwide and an online program for all levels of nursing. Chamberlain's mission statement about creating compassionate nurses aligned with what DAISY was all about. They had become one of our industry partners and brought in DAISY soon after they learned about us. (Years later Susan invited us to speak at Chamberlain's graduation—a highlight of our speaking careers.)

In the end, we had six deans join us on a call to the AACN. Together we talked about how faculty recognition might help mitigate the very real issues facing nursing colleges—things like faculty burnout, retention, and retirements. AACN CEO Deb Trautman listened and agreed to issue the national call that October, after which we doubled the number of schools participating. We know we'll never get all 800 AACN members, but we're motivated to get as many as we can—and as many of the nurses granted associate degrees at schools that are members of the Organization of Associate Degree Nurses, which also supports DAISY faculty recognition. Because no matter what the future of nursing brings, the human touch will never be automated in our lifetimes. Robots may one day take over the world, but they are a long way from learning compassion—and for humans many schools still don't really teach compassion. Until they do, the DAISY Faculty

Award can help fill the void—for current and future teachers and nurses. Getting the new DAISY recognition programs going showed us why we had to remain students of nursing in order to continue to serve nurses everywhere. Which is why it should not be the least bit surprising that we also created an award for nursing students.

Shortly after we launched the DAISY Faculty Award, students at the University of Iowa sent us a PowerPoint presentation asking if we could add an award for them called the DAISY in Training Award. DAISY had been very successful at the University of Iowa Hospitals and Clinics for a long time, and the students had seen it there. We listened carefully to what these students had to say. They were concerned that with all the technology and clinical learning they were doing, they needed to be reminded why they wanted to be nurses in the first place. They knew nursing was not all clinical tasks and textbook learning. They were doing clinical rotations. They knew compassionate care had a profound impact on patients.

Another slap-your-forehead moment. We loved everything about the idea but the name. We changed it to the DAISY Award for Extraordinary Nursing Students. And while we were thinking about nurses at the start of their careers, why not add something at the end?

In 2018, Janet Rice, our DAISY Coordinator at UPMC Hamot, a hospital in Erie, Pennsylvania, asked if it would be okay if they honored a nurse who was retiring with a DAISY Award and a *Healer's Touch* sculpture as a gift. "She has worked here for 40 years," Janet said. "She has touched everything and every one of us. We have to do something for her. What would you think of a lifetime achievement award?"

"Duh," Mark replied.

"Why didn't we think of that?" Bonnie added.

Thus, the DAISY Lifetime Achievement Award was born, and it was a smash. We awarded more than 80 of them in 2019, its first full year.

So you see, on our 20th anniversary, DAISY is no longer turnkey thanks to the nurses who have defined DAISY's evolution. But that's perhaps not the most important lesson that nurses taught us as they owned and expanded the reach of the foundation. We have always said nurses are nurses everywhere. The important lesson nurses have taught us is that a DAISY Nurse is a DAISY Nurse no matter what award they receive.

Yes, DAISY's awards are each different in some way, as are the *Healer's Touch* sculptures that go with them. The nurse leader *Healer's Touch* is a little larger with a small twist, compared to the original sculpture, to reflect the indirect care they give. The student award is a little smaller than the original. The Lifetime Achievement Award is a little larger than all of them and comes with a pin we had designed by a jeweler. The Team Honorees get a special plaque. Nurses didn't mind any of this. But to further distinguish the awards, we had initially divided all of them into two groups: The DAISY Award for Extraordinary Nurses and the DAISY Awards for everything else. But nurses didn't. No matter what award they received, they called it the DAISY Award. Because they saw it as the same award.

This was another epiphany to us. Maybe that means we're not as smart as we never thought we were. In all seriousness, it means that nurses made DAISY not just bigger and better but more complex than we could possibly have understood when we came up with the idea for DAISY at that liquid dinner. We don't just have these different awards in hospitals and nursing schools. We're in all kinds of clinics, healthcare organizations, staffing agencies, and businesses that employ nurses—places completely outside of our original vision, so every nurse anywhere has the opportunity to be recognized and celebrated by their nursing colleagues in front of their teams, physicians, coworkers, and many times the patients who nominate them. When their powerful stories of compassionate care, as told by those who nominate them, are read aloud for all to hear, they comprehend the impact they make every day. No matter the award, they tell us that receiving a DAISY was a meaningful milestone in their nursing careers. They enable us to understand the power of meaningful recognition that DAISY represents.

But nurses didn't just help us understand this anecdotally. They also gave DAISY evidence that meaningful recognition makes a difference.

DAISY HONOREE STORY

The Emergency Department
Bethesda Hospital West
Boynton Beach, FL

I wanted to recognize an amazing team effort that occurred at Bethesda Hospital West on June 12, 2019. A patient presented to the Emergency Department with stroke symptoms. This patient is an urban outdoorsman, well known to the community and frequently seen by the hospital staff on their way to and from work. The patient had suffered a stroke and was being admitted to our hospital. He was the kindest gentleman and appreciative to all of the staff who were caring for him.

When it came time for the patient to be admitted to his room, he was reluctant to go. He has a companion dog named Chiquita and he did not want to leave her, knowing that he would have to send her to the nearest shelter. One of the nurses reassured him that she would take care of Chiquita so he could concentrate on getting better. She took the dog into her home, had it groomed, fed it well, even some filet mignon. This nurse came in on her days off to bring Chiquita for a visit with the patient. This put the patient at ease and allowed him to continue with his recovery. He realized that his Chiquita was being pampered beyond belief and in good hands.

Another Emergency Department team member began looking into getting this patient his social security and disability benefits. The staff knew a little bit about this gentleman but learned a great deal more about him during their care for his well-being. They learned that he had been a hard-working truck driver/roofer who became ill and was then unable to work. He had applied for Medicare disability but was denied. He then assumed that he was not eligible for any benefits. Being from Puerto Rico, he had no family support, no income, and soon adjusted to outdoor living. The team collaborated together to file the necessary paperwork, apply for Medicare, and certify Chiquita as a therapy pet. The registration staff member bought Chiquita her therapy vest. She also realized that with the patient suffering from neuro deficits due to his stroke, that he would need different clothing. Clothing that didn't have buttons, pants without zippers and shoes without laces. She purchased these items for him along with socks, underwear, and toiletries.

The team also had a hairdresser donate their time and come to the hospital to provide the patient with a fresh haircut and shave. The nurses also opened up a post office box for this gentleman so he could begin receiving his benefits. A phone was also purchased for him using Safe Link. This team continues to watch over this man, even after he was discharged from the hospital, many weeks later. They make sure he has his medications and is receiving his follow-up appointments as well as looking for the proper housing for him.

Because of this team's valiant efforts, this man has been able to continue his recovery with dignity, feeling that people do care for him.

"Every day we have multiple opportunities to recognize nursing excellence but in our busy schedules and fast-paced environments, we fail to do so. The DAISY Award helps us focus on this important aspect of our practice—celebrating nurses who provide compassionate, sensitive, and evidence-based care to patients and families."

Margie Sipe, DNP, RN, NEA-BC

Shining a New Light

The night Patrick involuntarily extubated his ventilator and blood went flying everywhere as the tube came out remains one of the most upsetting things we have ever seen or experienced. Tana, our nurse that night, took complete control of the situation—and us. And after she had everything reported and under control, she gave each of us a hug. That was the first time we learned that nurses give the best hugs.

Tana's hug is still with us today, as are the hugs of so many nurses we've met over the years. Countless other families and patients would say the same thing about their nurses' hugs. After all, hugs are the most human, physical manifestation of the relationship nurses have with patients and their families. They can mean as much as any act of compassion DAISY recognizes.

What hugs are *not* is scientific proof of the impact nurses make and the value of the meaningful recognition DAISY offered. And as DAISY grew, we began being asked for that, especially by nurse leaders and researchers. *Where is the evidence that shows meaningful recognition advances nursing practice? Where is the research that shows the DAISY Award will accomplish something significant for our staffs?* Evidence, evidence, evidence, evidence. Research, research, research, research. Even as we approached 1,000 hospitals, these words and questions about them followed us.

Not that we dismissed the need for evidence and research or their importance to nursing. We surely respected that in nursing, evidence-based practice means ensuring that patient care techniques are based on evidence grounded in scientific method. That's essential. But what makes nurses and nursing exceptional is a blend of clinical excellence and the art of compassion—the intuitive, intimate, real understanding of patients and families that comes from listening and paying attention to them. Nurses get this, especially DAISY Nurses, who have been honored by those patients and families. Yet even some DAISY Nurses were looking for research and evidence-based projects on meaningful recognition and how DAISY worked.

There was some evidence for the importance of meaningful recognition as DAISY grew. In 2005, the American Association of Critical-Care Nurses (AACN) cited meaningful recognition as one of six evidence-based standards for healthy and productive work environments along with skilled communication, true collaboration, effective decision making, appropriate staffing, and authentic leadership. "Nurses must be recognized and must recognize others for the value each brings to the work of the organization," the AACN stated at the time, and later reinforced with updated research in 2016. The AACN concluded that to be effective, recognition should be delivered through a formal process and program—exactly what DAISY does. But we were in our infancy when the AACN did its research. The standards affirmed the significance of what we did and aligned with the purpose of our work. But of the six AACN standards, meaningful recognition had the least amount of information and literature behind it.

With nurses owning and defining our direction more and more every day, we knew we needed to address this. But no metrics, let alone research studies or evidence-based projects, existed to even guide us on how to approach a study of the value of recognition for compassionate care. Our evidence was anecdotal, coming from the thousands of nurse leaders honoring their nurses and those nurses telling us about the feeling they got being honored with or just being nominated for a DAISY Award. How do you measure a feeling? How do you quantify a hug? It would be up to us to delve more deeply into the impact of our program for the evidence some nurses wanted and to better comprehend what DAISY was actually accomplishing for them and their organizations. Thanks to Dianne's work to capture the stories, we had thousands of nominations to explore. We just didn't know how to do it.

That's when the gods of nursing smiled on us once again: We met Cindy Lefton. Her work would provide the first evidence DAISY needed, and her words would inspire the title of this book.

We first met Cindy at the 2008 AONE Annual Conference, our first time at a conference. We attended a session copresented by Laura Caramanica, then the chief nursing officer at Westchester Medical Center in New York, which was a DAISY partner. The presentation focused on nurses' satisfaction with support services like housekeeping, and was based on results from a survey that had been done at 42 hospitals including Westchester. When the session ended, we congratulated Laura on her presentation and told her how fascinated we were by the evidence she presented. We mentioned that we were looking to generate a more evidence-based understanding of DAISY's impact.

"We want to put some science behind DAISY," Bonnie said.

Standing next to Laura was a woman we had never met before listening intently. Laura pointed in her direction, "Talk to her."

The woman looked at us and said, as we recall, "I know we have never met but I know about your work. I'm an organizational psychologist and a trauma nurse. I think you're onto something here. I'd love to do that study for you."

Are you serious?

She said she was, and introduced herself as Cindy Lefton. She worked at Psychological Associates in St. Louis, a well-respected firm founded by her father that helps clients select, develop, and retain talent. "I was at AONE to go to a presentation we had been involved in for Westchester Medical Center and wanted to thank Laura who was one of the presenters," Cindy says today. "I was standing there while she was talking to Bonnie, and she looked at and then pointed to me and said, 'Talk to her.' But I don't know that I knew much about what the DAISY Foundation was because they were still pretty new. Bonnie and I continued talking as a result of that conversation, however, and we eventually gave them a proposal for something like $40,000. They were surprised, but Psychological Associates is a for-profit business. That's what the study was worth."

We told Cindy we couldn't afford that. While the idea of doing research was very exciting, as full-time volunteers with very lean finances that we had just stabilized by having organizations pay for DAISY, we didn't see how we could pay tens of thousands of dollars for a full-blown research study.

Then something miraculous happened. Cindy said, "Well, we'll just do it for free." We know that sounds incredible—almost unbelievable. Nope.

"The more I thought about the study, the more I realized it was really important. It needed to be done," Cindy recalls. "I'm a nurse, and I know nurses always get positive feedback from their patients. Even as healthcare pushes to get people out of the hospital quicker, those endearing relationships are created. They still matter. But until DAISY, the words were just spoken in some amazing situation and then the nurses went on to the next patient and the next one. It keeps going, and going, and going. Nurses don't really talk about our days to nonhealthcare people because it's too hard to explain, so all that feedback was getting lost. What researching DAISY allowed me to do was give a bigger voice to these thousands of patients and families who told these nurses how important they were—that they matter and that they make a difference. DAISY had all these nominations with all this powerful positive feedback, and people still weren't focusing on the power of positive feedback. It connected the dots between what nurses are doing right and why it matters."

In Cindy's opinion, nurses weren't spending enough time on the "right." Most of the time nurses are focused on the "wrong." What's wrong with this patient. What's wrong with this piece of equipment. What went wrong with this situation. Something goes wrong and nurses spend countless hours on root cause analyses. But what happens when something goes right? Nothing. No meeting to analyze it and consider the impact of the positive. DAISY captured that positive and made nurses stop and celebrate the things they do well not just from the clinical side but from the human side.

"The DAISY Award brings to light the right," Cindy said. Bringing to light the right. What a perfect way to say what DAISY does. Cindy would shine that light on what we do in a way we never could: applying organizational psychology principles and behavioral science to examine the positive feedback and meaningful recognition behind DAISY. We were awed not only by Cindy's connection to our work but by the scope of her study: 2,195 blinded DAISY Award nominations from 20 locations analyzed; 42 randomly selected DAISY Award Honorees and 21 chief nursing officers interviewed. Of course Cindy was only doing what she does so brilliantly and what was expected of her in the field. What she didn't expect was how moved she would be by her research—so moved that she decided to go back into nursing.

"I read every single nomination," Cindy remembers. "One night I was sitting in my office, reading. I'd never seen rich data like that. I have a little bit of a background in customer service. I'm sitting there looking at this thinking, 'If Walmart or FedEx had stuff like this, they'd go nuts.' I was so taken emotionally. I started to cry at one of the nominations because it was so beautiful. I thought, 'You know what? I belong back in the hospital.' I actually flipped my career at that point. I went from working full-time at Psychological Associates to working part-time there and being a nurse again part-time at a hospital."

Like most studies, Cindy's took years to complete, write up, and get published, but in late 2012, it finally came out: "Strengthening the Workforce Through Meaningful Recognition" appeared in the November-December issue of *Nursing Economic$*. The results were beyond our wildest dreams, the effect impossible to overstate. Cindy's study changed the way DAISY was perceived by the broader nursing community. It put the strength of research behind what we had said from the beginning: Giving patients, families, and coworkers a way to genuinely express gratitude for the extraordinary compassionate care they received meant more to nurses and organizations than just the award itself.

The first point in Cindy's executive summary said it all: "Meaningfully recognizing the extraordinary contributions of nurses is a key element in creating and sustaining healthy work environments." Her study broke that down into four key findings:

1. The meaningful recognition process can elevate the value of nursing by providing patients, family members, and colleagues with a vehicle to recognize the extraordinary work of nurses.
2. Through a formalized meaningful recognition process, patients, family members, and colleagues can provide in their own words real-time feedback describing what mattered to them during their hospitalization and identify how behaviors of an extraordinary nurse made a difference.
3. Providing patients, families, and peers with a process to recognize nurses in a meaningful manner augments patient satisfaction data by illuminating the "detail" associated with these scores.

4. Formally recognizing extraordinary nursing through celebration can assist in shaping and driving an organization's culture and strengthening one's workforce.

"Whether it's shock and awe, demonstrating pride in one's work, nourishing a team, reaffirming the ministry of nursing, realizing the value of one's contributions, or reigniting a person's career," Cindy wrote, "this research provides the evidence that meaningful recognition can indeed strengthen a workforce."

We will never forget reading those words. For the first time we had an understanding of not just what it meant for us to say thank you to nurses but what it meant to the nurses to be thanked. Those four points transformed the way DAISY was perceived by nurse-researchers and anyone in nursing and beyond who wanted a side of science with all they were seeing in and feeling from the DAISY Awards. They reached chief nursing officers who needed more proof that DAISY would accomplish something significant for their staffs. As an experienced qualitative researcher, Cindy's expert insight into our nomination stories showed how they reflected what patients truly value and painted a vivid picture of what "extraordinary" care looks like. Themes of compassion, contagious positive attitude, calming presence, and connection to the family were among the top ten themes she identified. These nomination themes focused on *how* care was provided and what it meant.

A mom of a frightened child recalls how her sick little girl was distracted by her nurse who sang songs from *Frozen* to her while he handled her difficult IV insertion. This calmed her daughter and gave the mom a sense of trust that the nurse really cared about her child. A dressing change for a seriously burned man describes how his nurse knew how to minimize his extreme pain. The nurse listened to the patient, taking special care to do it in the exact way the patient could handle. An inspirational quote delivered by a nurse to a suicidal, depressed, and deeply anxious veteran patient showed the respect this person deserved and inspired him to work to get better. Because the nurse wanted to make a difference in the lives of those who have served our country.

These stories and thousands of others show how DAISY Honorees stand as role models, providing exemplars of nursing practice that can be used to set expectations for performance—for clinical competence and also for the human connection that is at the core of nursing practice. The science and the art of nursing, the delicate balance that makes a great difference to a patient's care experience. Care that other nurses are inspired to emulate.

Cindy's research also showed that the DAISY Awards enriched patient satisfaction scores because they provided organizations a treasure trove of qualitative data. When those organizations took the time to celebrate the "right" going on and implemented an ongoing, structured program of meaningful recognition like DAISY, it transcended the limitations and deepened their understanding of their quantitative patient satisfaction survey scores. After all, how do you put a "1 to 5" score on a patient writing "My nurse gave me the will to live"?

Cindy's final point about strengthening the workforce and its connection to DAISY was perhaps the most rewarding point to us as it showed how our recognition program contributes to the emotional rewards for nurses around the country. Nurses and especially nurse leaders constantly told us their DAISY Award celebrations—not just their own DAISY Awards but those for every nurse celebrated at the organization—were the best part of their days. Sharing nurses' stories throughout the year in a formal setting with an integrity-rich structure reminded nurses why they became nurses, toiled in nursing school, worked shifts they didn't probably didn't choose to work early in their careers, and dealt with the myriad pressures that healthcare is throwing at them day in and day out. Knowing that patients, family members, or colleagues took the time to write their stories of compassionate care made unbearable days a little more bearable for them. DAISY's meaningful recognition could not affect the concerning national trend of nursing shortages, but now we at least knew how it could help retain nurses already in the workforce. Cindy knew on a personal and scientific level how desperately that was and is needed.

"People are pretty tired," Cindy says, thinking about her work today. "The turnover in new nurses is just horrific. When I see them clocking out at the end of a 12-hour shift with that look in their eye, that they're so tired and they don't feel like they've made a difference . . . it saddens me that they don't realize the difference that they have made. Workplace violence is very prevalent, particularly in emergency departments. There's a lot of challenges with people who have behavioral health issues because there's not enough facilities across the country. No nurse should ever walk out at the end of their shift without recognizing something good that they did—the difference that they made in somebody's life. DAISY is nursing's best cheerleader."

Actually patients and families are nursing's best cheerleaders. We humbly facilitate a program that enables their stories to be shared and recognizes all the good that is happening every day. But before Cindy's study, we had no way to shine a scientific light on how DAISY has changed cultures to emphasize acts of compassionate care. Now we had a new tool in our toolbox: a research study to show how meaningful recognition advances nursing practice and how nurses are inspired to advance their practice through DAISY. And Cindy's study wouldn't be the last.

After Cindy Lefton's study was published and presented at the Magnet conference, AONE's annual meeting, the AACN's National Teaching Institute, and elsewhere, a robust body of evidence demonstrating DAISY's impact was built—studies on the impact of meaningful recognition on a healthy work environment, nurse engagement, compassion fatigue and compassion satisfaction, how recognition affects the patient and family experience, and more.

Cindy and Lesly Kelly completed a mixed-method study to explore DAISY's impact on compassion fatigue. Cindy's qualitative portion interviewed 90-plus ICU nurses on what recharges their emotional energy. Four themes emerged: Nurses are recharged emotionally when they are thanked; see their patients improve clinically; know their team members have their back; and become aware that they have made a difference they didn't know they had made. The DAISY Award covered three of these four themes. The quantitative portion of this research, led by Lesly, revealed, among other things, that nurses who had received nominations for DAISY Awards had lower compassion fatigue and higher compassion satisfaction.

Chamberlain University did a study on the DAISY Faculty Award and their president, Susan Groenwald, cited it in her book *Designing & Creating a Culture of Care for Students and Faculty*. There is research that connects the kind of meaningful recognition DAISY offers as it relates to an organization's return on investment: A study by Laura McClellan and Timothy Vogus out of Virginia Commonwealth University found that "when a hospital explicitly rewards compassionate acts by its staff and supports its staff during tough times, it is associated with patients more highly rating the care experience and being more likely to recommend the hospital." And there are several studies in the works as we head into our 21st year, including the national rollout of a pilot study that Cindy Lefton did with, Susan Grant, Cindy Sweeney (DAISY's vice president for nursing), and Melissa Foreman-Lovell. The pilot addressed a question we had been asking for several years: What does it mean to patients and families to say thank you to their nurses by writing a DAISY nomination? The findings of the pilot study show that patients and families feel connected to the organization through the nomination and recognition of their nurse, which may contribute to loyalty for the organization and increased likelihood to recommend it as a healthcare organization of choice.

There are many more studies we could cite here, not that we or the organizations that have implemented DAISY *need* more evidence. The primary goal of additional evidence is understanding: to shine the scientific and artistic light on all the right that nurses do and help those who don't see that right in themselves—or in each other. The additional goal is also for DAISY and all who work for and connect to us after twenty years to understand and articulate our impact. To that end, we developed what we call the DAISY Model of Impact.

The model was inspired by Cindy Sweeney, whom we hired in 2014. We had known Cindy since 2009 from ANCC, where she had been a director and run the Magnet conference. Her nursing and research background allowed her to use all we knew about DAISY to express as simply as possible how, as a form of meaningful recognition, DAISY can impact the organization. Cindy sketched on the back of an envelope what became the three "sides" of DAISY's triangle of impact: a Healthy Work Environment, Nurse Engagement, and the Patient/Family Experience. Each of these sides was informed by all the evidence we had and would receive in the years to come.

But while all three sides of the triangle are essential to the impact of DAISY's meaningful recognition on the nurses and the organizations we support, for all of us it always comes back to the stories—stories of nurses who are proficient in the relational aspects of nursing. Who understand how their care profoundly affects their patients and families and moves the patient/family experience into the realm of the extraordinary. Cindy Sweeney, Bonnie, and Mary Koloroutis said exactly that as the authors of DAISY's first white paper in 2015, "Inspiring Nurses to See the Extraordinary in the Ordinary." Yes, nurses will say what they often say when presented with a DAISY Award, "I was just doing my job—I was just doing what I do every day." They don't see the extraordinary in their ordinary. But you can't even spell extraordinary without ordinary.

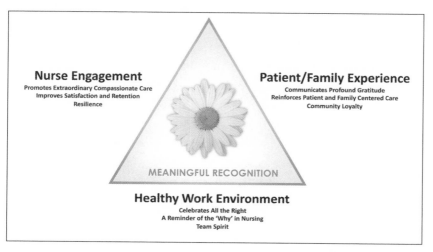

The DAISY Impact Model

Shining the Light on All the Right

Cindy Lefton said one of her favorite stories she tells in her speeches is about an older terminally ill patient who only wanted a fruit plate. The way this woman described the importance of this fruit plate when she was nearing the end of her life showed how such a small thing can be so important. One nurse made sure she had it when she wanted it and was honored with a DAISY Award for her compassion. She was shocked. It was just a fruit plate. It was no big deal to arrange for it. Yet the nomination noted that several other nurses *didn't* do it before she did. The DAISY Nurse understood its importance, and hopefully in seeing her being presented her award, the other nurses who missed how little things make a difference will understand it, too.

Simply put: Many, many nurses and healthcare professionals don't need a white paper, research study, or evidence-based project to understand the significance of that nurse who delivered the fruit plate and hundreds of thousands, if not millions, of other nurses who perform those compassionate acts every day. We never appreciated this more than when we spoke at the Royal College of Surgeons School of Nursing and Midwifery in Dublin, Ireland. Most of the speakers who preceded us were scientific nurses doing wonderful talks on their very important research. They all received robust rounds of applause. When we spoke about DAISY, we did not focus on our research. We told our story and the stories of the nurses who received DAISY Awards. To our shock we received a standing ovation. Thomas Kearns, executive director of the Faculty of Nursing and Midwifery of the Royal College, explained why: "Some things you don't need the scientific evidence for. Some things are just so obviously right to do."

From the very beginning of DAISY, our goal was to express our heartfelt personal appreciation for the difference nurses made in our lives and the lives of their patients and their patients' families. Nurses make a big difference in the lives of others, so we did our best to make a difference in theirs. Nothing makes us prouder than to have stayed true to that mission.

DAISY HONOREE STORY

Nikole Kessler, BSN, RN
Penn Highlands Healthcare–DuBois
DuBois, Pennsylvania

Nikole shared in our tears as they turned from heartache to tears of joy and hope. Our child was born in January. She was diagnosed with trisomy 18, incompatible with life. We knew that she would be cared for at the NICU after she was born due to her diagnosis. What we didn't know was how much she would be loved and cared for by the staff.

Our baby was placed on a ventilator due to episodes of apnea and had more wires, tubes, and monitors than could be imagined. It was hard to deal with. It was difficult to see our baby going through so much. But what wasn't difficult to see was the compassion and love she received from the nurses and also the huge impact that this small life had on them, as well as us. We will never forget the NICU nurses and all the memories we had with them. They will always be a part of our family and we are forever grateful for them.

Nikole Kessler cared for our baby through the best times and hardest times. She laughed with us, celebrated with us, and even cried with us. She was able to look past all the wires and tubes and only saw our baby. You could see a connection growing between the two. She not only took care of her as a nurse, she cared for her as if she was her own. She wasn't afraid of our baby's condition. As a matter of fact, she took it on as a challenge. Our baby would beat the odds and be her "feisty spice." She made sure that she received the best care and all the snuggles she could give.

Nikole walked with us hand in hand through our baby's entire journey in the NICU. Just four days after her birth, we had to make a heartbreaking decision to discontinue the ventilator. We couldn't have our baby live on a vent for the rest of her days. Nikole stayed with us, even off duty, through that difficult time. She took a turn holding her and cried right with us as we thought our baby's time here on Earth was over. Nikole even hand-made a wooden plaque for this day, "Too Beautiful for Earth." As the minutes turned to hours and our baby amazed us all with a desire to live, breathing on her own, Nikole shared in our tears as they turned from heartache to tears of joy and hope.

The following day Nikole checked on our baby as soon as she came into the NICU, to make sure she made it through the night. She kept us updated through her entire shift and shared in our joy and relief as she continued to report that her vitals were stable and she was not having any episodes of apnea.

Nikole made sure we didn't miss any special moments. She carried the camera in her pocket and was quick to capture every significant second, the first time we fed our baby through her NG tube, her first outfit, first bath. She filled two photo books and ran the printer out paper just so we had every memory of the beginning and what we thought would be the end of her life.

Nikole continued to be there for our baby even on her days off of work. She made the trip into the hospital and spent hours with her just to hold her.

Finally, the day came when we were able to take our baby home and Nikole was there to do her discharge. There wasn't a dry eye in the NICU, especially Nikole's. She even escorted her out of the hospital just so she could soak up every last moment with her.

To this day Nikole continues to be a part of our child's life, keeping up with her and all of her firsts and celebrating with us every time she defies the odds. Nikole is more than the NICU nurse who cared for our baby, she is part of our family and we know Nikole will forever be a part of her life as long as our child is with us on this journey.

"There is such powerful transformation that occurs for each nurse who learns that he/she was nominated and then even more so for the monthly recipient. The DAISY Award provides us with an opportunity to pause each month on a unit with the winner and peers and share how 'simple' nursing actions, caring, listening, and acknowledging are so critical to our patients and families."

Katherine Pakieser-Reed, PhD, RN

All We Wanted to Do Was Say Thank You

After a 2019 speaking engagement and dinner in Maine, we had to drive from Central Maine Medical Center in Lewiston to a bed-and-breakfast owned by a nurse in Bridgeton. The drive was only 35 miles inland, but we had spent well over an hour trying to find our way through the middle-of-Maine night. The same darkness that enveloped us also enveloped the navigation apps on our devices.

Shining the Light on All the Right

We were with our Northeast Regional Program Director, Alex Schoen, and each of us was using a different GPS. At each stop sign, Apple, Garmin, and Google told us to go in a different direction until we came to a fork in the road. Yogi Berra famously said when you come to a fork in the road, take it. Not even Yogi could help us now. All our devices said take the dirt road between the branches of the fork. It was 9:30 P.M. We could see nothing around us. We decided to trust what we saw and took the road less travelled—and unmarked—and ended up right where we belonged.

So has DAISY. We chose to take an unpaved and unmarked road to recognizing the nurses who had been so kind and delivered such compassionate care to us, our family, and Our Patrick in the weeks before he died.

Over the years, people have told us that choosing to emphasize this compassion in our recognition for nurses was an "innovation," but we didn't see it as all that inventive. All we wanted to do was say thank you. But unlike that night in Maine, we had no idea where we were going when we started—and no GPS could help us. Nothing like the DAISY Awards existed in the nursing world. We never imagined that 20 years later more than 4,000 organizations and colleges of nursing in the United States and 25 other countries would share our mission. At one point we didn't think we would make 50 hospitals in five years! We never intended to create DAISY Awards in six different categories. We never expected to have research studies published about the impact of our meaningful recognition—and to publish our own. Sure, we envisioned grants to support research—but to find a cure for ITP, not the myriad research of 100-plus nurse-led studies. That we would have a staff of 22 and 30 board members over the years supporting us and nurses still amazes us every day.

And we certainly never dreamed that we would receive more than 1.6 million DAISY Award nominations and honor 136,000 individuals and teams and counting by the end of our 20th year. Clearly, we were not the only family compelled to say thank you to nurses.

Shining the Light on All the Right

The vastness of DAISY today is hard for us to comprehend and even accept sometimes. We still don't quite know what to make of people saying DAISY has transformed the culture of their organizations. Or when someone calls us rock stars. Every year we find ourselves standing in front of audiences of esteemed, highly educated nurses of all walks who are dedicated to improving the care of patients and wonder what the heck are we doing there. How did we become honorary members of Sigma Theta Tau International Honor Society of Nursing, the second-largest nursing organization in the world? How do we deserve to be honorary fellows of the American Academy of Nursing? Or honorary members of the American Organization for Nursing Leadership, the Oncology Nursing Society, and the Association of Pediatric/Hematology Oncology Nurses? Recipients of the Pioneering Spirit Award of the American Association of Critical-Care Nurses, American Nurses Credentialing Center's (ANCC's) President's Award, and so many more we have accepted with a mix of honor and incredulity? How did we end up being saluted by ANCC in front of 10,000-plus nurses with a song performed by Lexi Walker and the Opera Orlando Chorus at the 2019 Magnet conference in celebration of our 20th anniversary?

Recognizing the recognition DAISY provides: Our embrace in front of nurses at the tribute to DAISY at ANCC's Magnet Conference in honor of our 20th anniversary, October 2019. Photo by Kenneth Krehbiel, Imageworks Photography.

Nurses giving us standing ovations—thanking *us?* DAISY may exist because of us, but DAISY prospered in our first 20 years because of nurses!

In those moments of disbelief, we stand backstage, hold each other's hands, push down any feeling that someone has made a terrible mistake, and walk out together as our names are announced. Well, all but the one at the American Academy of Nursing. Mark still kept thinking as we took the stage that these were the smartest smarty-pants of the nursing world and maybe they weren't as smart as we thought they were because they were honoring *us*—and as a couple, which had never happened before.

That day at the Academy we felt a tremendous physical closeness as we took in DAISY's acceptance and embrace by this profession for what we brought them. But as we said that day and every day before and since, DAISY is a two-way street, and nurses brought us more than we feel we brought them. Nurses not only took ownership of DAISY but defined and evolved it, doing more things than we could possibly recount in these pages. They developed DAISY display walls, DAISY carts for presentations, DAISY-reserved parking places, specially designed DAISY nomination boxes (one cleverly crafted to look like a Cinnabon), DAISY elevator door coverings, and DAISY cakes and cookies. Nurses made DAISY nomination signs for patients' rooms, to post throughout the hospital, to go home in discharge packets, and to post on their organizations' websites. They have DAISY-fied every article of clothing we could imagine from T-shirts to sweatshirts to aprons to jackets. We've seen DAISY badge pulls, lanyards, water bottles, coffee cups, balloons, and . . . ice sculptures! Then the nurses spread awareness of all this DAISY-fication by putting it and more on Facebook, Instagram, Twitter, YouTube, and every other form of social media we don't know anything about.

Yes, one time the nurses' creativity almost cost us a lot of money when their hospital placed a picture of a field of daisies on its nomination form. We thought it was gorgeous so we copied the photo and sent it out to all the hospitals at the time to use. Turns out it wasn't their photo. They'd copied it from a stock photo company that contacted

Cinnamon roll DAISY nomination box, Morton Plant Mease
Health Care, Clearwater, FL

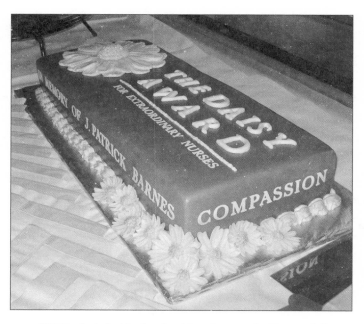

DAISY cake baked by the daughter of a nurse for Thomas Jefferson
University Methodist Hospital, Philadelphia

DAISY elevators, Lower Keys Medical Center, Key West, FL

us and asked for $30,000 for permission to use it in all the hospitals. Thankfully they settled for $300. (Someone there probably had a story of an extraordinary nurse.)

Most of the time, however, the creativity just makes us smile and costs nothing, like the DAISY Award ceremony at Grady Memorial in downtown Atlanta. When we visited years ago, Rhonda Scott, then the chief nursing officer, gathered her senior leaders for every DAISY presentation and they carried pompoms and a boom box through the hospital to surprise the DAISY Nurse by playing Tina Turner's "Simply the Best." Nurses have also welcomed us in unforgettable ways, like at Bronson Methodist Hospital in Kalamazoo, Michigan. The nurses gathered in a room filled with daisy plants, and after the award presentation, they picked up the flowers and planted them in a DAISY garden.

Like the daisies in that garden today, DAISY got here because of nurses. We thrive because of the nurse leaders who tell us what DAISY means to them; how the days DAISY is on their calendars are their favorite days of the month; and how their DAISY Honorees' stories make them indescribably proud of their staffs as they marvel at their compassion and excellence. We succeed because of the DAISY Coordinators and DAISY Committees who are dedicated to bringing our program to life month after month when they have oh-so-much-else to do. The nurses and others who fill those roles are passionate about DAISY and bring their creativity and resourcefulness to ensure its success in their organizations. They care so much for the nurses on their staffs and know they deserve to have every DAISY Award presentation be an unforgettable experience.

And of course we got here because of the extraordinary care provided by and recognized in our DAISY Award Honorees and Nominees. When we ask them why they committed their lives to nursing, what they talk about is taking care of patients. Of being in that sacred, trusted space when people are at their most vulnerable. We can see that their outstanding clinical judgment and expertise, honed over years of education, training, and experience, is inextricably linked to the compassionate care we so profoundly admire and celebrate. Nurses even tell us they hold—and must remember to hold—themselves differently when they become DAISY Nurses. One nurse told us that soon after she received her award she was having a bad day and feeling grumpy. One of the other nurses said, "You can't act like that anymore. You're a DAISY Nurse." These words really resonated with her, and she realized she had to hold herself to a higher standard—that a DAISY Award came with extra responsibility and accountability.

DAISY has come with new responsibility and accountability for us, too. We see ourselves as DAISY's facilitators, but also its gatekeepers. Mark never fails to ask questions about any innovation, award, partnership, sponsorship, and relationship no matter how perfect it seems to align with what we do. *Do we want to do this? Is this in line with our message? Is this DAISY?* We have been very clear about our strategy for anyone who wants to work with us. First and foremost they have to love nurses. Any conversation that mentions the importance of return on investment, not an appreciation of all nurses do, gets politely shut down. The value of DAISY is implicit in the meaningful recognition we offer, and we are looking for relationships based on an understanding of that. We have discontinued and rejected sponsors that didn't get this—or just didn't feel right. We believe staying true to these principles and our mission is why DAISY has a remarkable 96 percent retention rate. Even organizations that get sold or hospitals that merge with a larger group that doesn't have DAISY have stayed with us.

Our private life is also accountable to DAISY. We may aggressively discuss where we are going or how someone or something is doing—we have our challenges all the time just like any family and family business. But it is always based in gratitude and love for DAISY and each other—and respect. We made a deal at the beginning of this journey that whenever one of us had an idea, the other one had to respect it and work to implement it. That said, Bonnie will tell you she couldn't keep up with Mark's ideas. Bonnie's the thinker—the writer and public speaker. She may cry at every new DAISY creation she sees, but she leads with her head. Mark may ask all those questions and be the business strategist for DAISY, but he leads with his heart. It's a balance that has allowed us to grow DAISY together without "killing" each other. We could not love it or each other more. DAISY is our passion and we share it with the world, *together*. In fact, we don't do anything DAISY without doing it together; most people never see us apart. One time Bonnie had to go to a conference alone because a dog had bit Mark and he couldn't travel. This was quite disorienting for the attendees, and Bonnie spent all four days answering one question: "Where's Mark?"

People those days may have wondered where Mark was, but like that night driving in Maine, we can say with absolute certainty that we, like DAISY, have ended up right where we belong: at home with the nurses.

And still to this day, those nurses will tell us everything we experienced with Patrick was just them doing their jobs. That it was nothing special. We want to say one last time that when you are a patient or a family member, in a heightened state of emotion and feeling helpless and quite scared and you watch a great nurse in action, the work they do is special. It's sacred. It's meaningful. It makes a difference and has an impact. It deserves recognition. It deserves respect.

Our greatest hope is that DAISY somewhere, somehow makes one more person realize the power of meaningful recognition—to a nurse for sure, but also to a colleague, stranger, friend, loved one, or someone who simply did something right by you. If we can put one more genuine, heartfelt thank-you in this world, then we have shone a little more light on the right people do. The importance of genuine, authentic recognition for even the little things people do, without any expectation of return, to make your life or the life of someone you love better, is something that cannot be discounted in this world. It seems so easy to do but we are all so pressed for time and thinking about what is going wrong that we forget the power of a simple thank-you.

Twenty years after our liquid dinner, we can't imagine a life without DAISY even though it means we have to accept that we have lost Our Patrick. But we are comforted every day by the feeling that he is with us in spirit and proud of all DAISY has become. He would be thrilled that people know his name and his story. And we know what he would say to us if he could. They're the same words he would say to all his nurses: *Thank you.*

DAISY HONOREE STORY

Katherine Shive, BSN, RN

Baptist Health Louisville

Louisville, Kentucky

Katherine decorated the patient's room and made the patient her own personal beach sanctuary. To top it all off, the patient was able to fulfill her last wish—to be able to have her feet in the sand one last time.

There are always those patients who change you—those patients and families who break your heart and remind you why you first became a nurse. Recently, there was a young patient in our unit who was suffering from advanced-stage esophageal cancer. She had been feeling ill for a while and ended up postponing coming into the hospital so she could be present for her daughter's graduation. By the time she got to our unit, she was in bad shape and needed to be rapidly intubated for respiratory distress. Katherine held her hand throughout the procedure assuring her that she was not alone and that she would be there to take care of her when she woke up from anesthesia.

Indeed, Katherine was there when she woke up and for the many nights that followed. She cared diligently for her and her family—titrating medications, calling physicians and adding drips, all while fetching blankets for the family and listening to their personal stories about their mother and wife. When the patient's condition continued to worsen and hope seemed to be lost, Katherine sat and grieved with the family whom she had become so close to. They talked about her life and what she had planned and what she would do if she had more time. With some thought, the patient wrote her a note that said, "I just want to walk on the beach one more time."

While I think we can all agree that this is very touching, many people would brush this off as an unrealistic last wish of a dying patient. Katherine, being her extraordinary self, did not. The very next day, Katherine came into work with her arms full of grocery bags. She had gone out after her shift and bought anything and everything that she could find relating to the beach—beach balls, palm tree wall hangings, sterile sand, and even beach-scented air freshener. She also went home and disinfected shells from her personal collection to bring in. With the family's blessing, Katherine decorated the patient's room and made the patient her own personal beach sanctuary. To top it all off, the patient was able to fulfill her last wish—to be able to have her feet in the sand one last time.

Sometimes, nursing is not about the patients we save, it is about the journey that we take as a healthcare team together. Because of Katherine's extraordinary care and love, the patient's family left this hospital knowing their wife and mother was loved, valued, and truly cared for. Katherine has always been an amazing nurse and this interaction proves that she is a true DAISY Nurse.

Facing the
Future

Fire

Friday, October 6, 2017. We had been at a conference in San Antonio and were scheduled to be in Houston on Tuesday. We debated whether we should just spend the weekend in Texas and visit friends, but decided to go home for the weekend.

The fires started on Sunday night.

Our first clue something was wrong was around midnight when one of our German shepherds, Max, started barking his head off. Max barks at things outside all the time, but not at night. We looked out the window and saw the orange glow of fire at the end of our vineyard behind the house. We thought it was a grass fire. Shaking off our sleep, we went outside to get hoses to put it out. The hoses didn't even have nozzles on them. We planned to use our thumbs to make a spray. Then we noticed trees were burning too, and the neighbor's lawn in flames. This was no grass fire. And it was coming towards us.

Bonnie tried calling 911 from her cell. Busy signal. They answered on the second try. The fire department arrived in minutes because they were posting a blockade at the end of our road. We were loading the dogs in the car as a fireman tromped across the yard in full equipment.

"Get out of here right now. Get in your cars, close the garage doors, and leave. We will try to save your house."

We grabbed the dogs and left. Our friends Joan and Jim Griffin took us in at their house in Petaluma. The next morning we all began to grasp the enormity of what would be known as the Northern California Wildfires of 2017: 250 of them that would eventually consume 250,000 acres that October in just four counties. The fires raged all Monday in our area of Sonoma Valley but by Tuesday they had shifted away, and we decided to try to get to our house to see what had become of it. We drove to the blockade with Erin Ascher, DAISY's executive assistant. The air was hideous, rancid and acrid, not the clean wood smoke of a campfire. No one could tell us if our house had survived.

We talked our way past the police, and as we walked up the hill toward our house, the scene that unfolded was more hideous than the air. It looked like our entire neighborhood had burned down. We got to the bottom of our driveway and started up, dreading what we might see. As we came around the bend, we saw our garage, which served as DAISY's warehouse and shipping department, was gone. Our hearts sank as we kept walking to the house. But it was safe—badly scorched in places, but safe. We looked back to where the garage had been. That's when we saw them. Surrounded by smoldering trees from the woods that used to be there and amidst the ashes and rubble of the garage, eight of the large *Healer's Touch* sculptures that more than 400 hospitals and organizations have bought for display in their lobbies and healing gardens as a tribute to the care their nurses provide. Prior to the fire, they were packed in their wooden crates, ready to be shipped. The crates had burned, but the stone carvings were standing tall and strong. *Look at that!*

"This is a sign," Erin said.

What it was a sign of we had no time to process at that time. The wind was picking up. We knew the fires could come back. We grabbed the stuff we needed from inside the house, used water from the jugs we stored on the porch to put out hot spots that were all over the place, and left once again.

The fires did come back, threatening the home Mark had lived in since 1970. But we thought about DAISY as much as we thought about anything else in there—our home and DAISY's were one and the same. More than 1,000 *Healer's Touch* sculptures and everything else that goes with the DAISY Awards that had been stored in the garage were already gone. They were replaceable, but inside the house were our offices, and Mark's was the DAISY Museum. Every shelf, cabinet, and bit of wall space and floor space was filled with the one-of-a-kind—the irreplaceable artifacts we have received and collected since DAISY's beginning. Everything the nurses, hospitals, colleges, and other organizations around the world had given us. Every award, letter, scrapbook, gift, and tchotchke. All we could do was pray the fires didn't cost us any more than they already had. They didn't.

Our house had caught fire, but the firefighters had put it out before it could do tragic damage. The hillsides all around our home and most of our neighbors' houses were incinerated. We were among the lucky ones. Nevertheless, we couldn't move back for six weeks until the fires were extinguished for good, power was restored, and a 2,500-gallon temporary water tank was delivered and hooked up. We could visit though, and every time we did, we saw those large *Healer's*

After the fire, *Healer's Touch* sculptures standing tall amid the rubble, October 2017

Touch sculptures on the burn pile. We thought about Erin calling them a sign. But of what? A phoenix, of course—DAISY rising from the ashes!

The phoenix analogy seemed perfect and also, we realized, wrong. DAISY was not a phoenix, because DAISY had not died upon this pyre. If everything we owned had burned to the ground that October, our loss would be personally devastating but DAISY would stand tall and strong like those *Healer's Touch* sculptures. DAISY was alive and well in offices and organizations around the world. The sculptures were not a sign of DAISY's rebirth. They were a sign of DAISY's resilience. We didn't need to keep DAISY going. DAISY *was* going . . . in Georgia, Washington, Michigan, Ohio, Maryland, Oklahoma, and other parts of California—states where our remarkable staff live—and in the hands of nurses at thousands of hospitals and organizations worldwide. They, like the intertwined figures in the sculptures, were holding DAISY up.

We may lovingly call our offices in our Sonoma home the DAISY Worldwide Headquarters, but DAISY had been more than Mark and

Bonnie Barnes for years. Long before the fires burned, we had told our board that we trusted them to keep DAISY going long after we are gone. They have assured us DAISY will live on in their hands and in their hearts. But so have our family, staff, the organizations who support us, and most importantly the nurses all over the world who would not let DAISY go. We heard those assurances over and over again from the nurses who reached out in the days and weeks following the fires to make sure we were okay. Their words lifted us up as we rebuilt and restocked. The messages made us feel that we were not just okay—we were strong and resilient. And so was DAISY. In response to all those wonderful messages and to reach as many nurses who shared their concern, we sent an email to 5,000-plus nurses with a picture of those *Healer's Touch* sculptures. We assured them that DAISY, like us, was alive and well and affirmed our commitment to nurses.

Nurses still talk about the photo today. How they shared it with the people in their lives. How it inspired them and gave them hope. Not us—the photo of the *Healer's Touch*. People tell us all the time that there's no stopping DAISY now—that it has "taken on a life of its own." The nurses' response to the photo was just further evidence that those people are right. But like we said, we knew that already. In fact, a year before, a more intimate moment showed us how much this was true. We were being honored at the Oncology Nursing Society's conference, and as we prepared to take the stage we heard the introduction.

"Ladies and gentlemen, Mark and Bonnie Barnes." Polite applause filled the room as the announcer paused. "Founders of the DAISY Foundation," the announcer continued. Everyone stood and cheered. Nothing could have made us happier: They didn't know who we were, but they sure knew DAISY.

Shining the Light on People Who Have Helped Make DAISY Right

Twenty Years of Gratitude

Creating this book has been a remarkable process, taking us back in time and reflecting on the many, many people, especially the nurses, who came into our lives and guided us on our DAISY journey.

When we first approached Jim Eber, our not-so-ghostlike writer about working on this project, he told us we were not ready for him yet. We needed to visualize the book—to be clear why we were doing it and know what our message would be. He asked us to spend a little more time thinking about some questions he gave us and then call him again. That conversation was inspirational! Bonnie started writing answers to his questions, and a few weeks later, Jim enthusiastically agreed it was time for us to get to work. He visited us in Glen Ellen, talked with us on the phone, and pored over 20 years of DAISY's work with us, capturing our stories along with our tears, our laughter, and our efforts to remember things that happened long ago. He spoke to the people who started this journey with us to find out what he—and we—did not know or remember. And then he created this book, which we believe speaks with our voice and DAISY's voice.

Jim, you have our heartfelt gratitude for sharing this journey with us and for making it so much fun. You and our team of publishing experts—Nathan and Shannon Jamail of Scooter Publishing, Suzanne Fass, Karen Billip of Eliot House Productions, and Jane Majkiewicz—have brought this book to life.

What joy we have had with Jim going through those memories, interviews, nominations, the many beautiful, well-crafted scrapbooks nurses have created for us over the years, and the thousands of thank-you's that our granddaughter Riley and our friend Ryan Maher assembled in big notebooks. Those notebooks and scrapbooks sit in the part of Mark's office we call the DAISY Museum along with the many gifts nurses and organizations have given us: stuffed animals, elaborate floral displays (now dried), Arabian boxes, porcelain cups, plaques, stunning glass awards, recognitions of DAISY from nursing's professional organizations . . . there's even a wonderful handmade Raggedy Ann.

Looking at the museum today, we realize just how many people and places fill our hearts. We could not possibly start to recount them all here or we'd have to print a second book! So where *do* we start to acknowledge some of the millions of people—yes, millions, if you count all DAISY nominees and the people who wrote their nominations—who have made DAISY *DAISY* over the last two decades? We start at the beginning and apologize deeply if we left anyone out! (Note: to make reading the names easier we have left out all credentials, titles, and ranks; to avoid any sense of favoritism, we have put lists of names in alphabetical order.)

✳ ✳ ✳

To Patrick's nurses: Your compassionate and skillful care for him and us is the reason there is a DAISY Award. We lament that we, like so many people for whom you care, left the hospital without saying a proper thank-you. We simply had to go once we said our last goodbye to him. But our gratitude to you all throughout those weeks right up to the time you walked us to the door one last time was immense and has only grown. No words will ever be able to express our appreciation. Karen Bidwell, Ann Blake, Andi Bowen, Patti Daraskavich, Susan Polizzi Dowling, Debra Goff, Andrea Hanses, Peggy Haug, Tana Irish, Ken Kanfoush, Karen Kuster, Diane Lynn, Lynn Maleta, Vivian Markle, Juanita Merriweather, Terrie Paine, Susan Pambianco, Peggy Stufflebeam, Debra Thomas, Jocelyne Wahl, Robert Young, and any others we missed, thank you. We hope we have done you proud with the DAISY work you inspired.

✳ ✳ ✳

To our family: Our love and respect for nurses is one of so many things we have in common in keeping Pat's spirit alive and present. The loss of Patrick was your loss, too, of course. Thank you for standing by our sides through all these years.

Tena Barnes Carraher and Dianne Barnes, you have been there since the beginning and served as board members, volunteers, and staff. What haven't you done for DAISY?

Adam Barnes, we would be buried in legal fees without you and your counsel.

Brad and Danna Barnes, you have participated in DAISY celebrations and introduced us to the hospital where Danna's dad was a physician.

Wayne, Shelley, Brandon, and Remy Baruch, you have listened to more stories of our DAISY adventures than anyone should have to—Wayne especially, as he has produced the Magnet Conference for many years, including the spectacular tribute to DAISY's first 20 years in 2019.

Dave Lauer, you and your late wife, Marilyn, served on our board and, with Dianne, facilitated DAISY presentations at our first hospital.

And of course, we are blessed to have the ongoing dedication of "Auntie Bonkers," Melissa Barnes.

Again, thank you all.

* * *

To the nurse leaders who have served on our board of directors: When we created the DAISY Award, we did it out of our need to say thank you to nurses. It didn't occur to us that nurses might benefit from this statement of gratitude. Several nurse leaders—pioneers in partnering with us—saw the value of recognizing compassionate care and the merit and strategic value of our mission. They joined our board and have been holding our hands ever since. The contributions of Cindy Angiulo, Ann Evans, Mary Dee Hacker, Susan Grant, and Beth Heyman have been documented in this book. Each of them has made a significant difference to DAISY, and we are grateful to them beyond words.

We are equally grateful for the contributions of the other nurses on our board.

To Cynthia Barginere: Your support started years ago when you were chief nursing officer at Rush University Medical Center. Today you are Rush's chief transformational officer, and we are so grateful you are there whenever we ask to help us understand the changing face of healthcare and how DAISY can and will continue to serve nurses.

To Stuart Downs: You developed the concept of giving a card to each DAISY Nominee signed by the chief nursing officer and introduced us to Chamberlain University. You brought DAISY from hospital to hospital with you along with your tradition of celebrating DAISY Nurses with DAISY ice sculptures filled with shrimp! Your love for DAISY is deep, and your strategic contributions to DAISY are many. We can't thank you enough.

To Kathy Gorman: From your early and energetic support for DAISY when you were at CHOP to always being the first to raise your hand for anything DAISY needs or wants to ensuring DAISY is front and center wherever you are to bringing your insights as chief operating officer at Children's National Medical Center, your influence on DAISY's behalf is extraordinary. You are always there for us, professionally and personally. Thank you for being our loving friend.

To Jane Kamstra: You left our board a few years ago, but you will never leave our lives or our hearts. You are a "nurse's nurse," and we are blessed to call you our friend.

To Karlene Kerfoot: You were the first chief nursing officer to bring DAISY to an entire healthcare system. Today, as the chief nursing officer at API Healthcare, you have taught us so much about the strategic value of meaningful recognition. Thank you for that, for always finding a way to include DAISY in your articles and presentations, and for your love and friendship.

To Deb Zimmermann: We were thrilled when you agreed to join our board. Your enthusiasm for DAISY and the support you give your staff running the program at Virginia Commonwealth University has been a big reason why DAISY gets hundreds of nominations each month there. Your brainpower and love for what we do make us better. Thank you!

❋ ❋ ❋

To the "non-nurses" who served on our board early on: You did more than provide us with excellent counsel. You believed in our mission and in some cases even introduced us to hospitals. Dianne Barnes, Tena Barnes Carraher, Norman Cohen, the late Lynne Doll, Judy and Bruce England, Mark Kamstra, Bonnie Lasky, Michael O'Neil, Mike Patterson, and Gayle and John Schofield, thank you from the bottom of our hearts.

To the thousands of other nurse leaders who have impacted us and whose wisdom has guided us, including *but not limited to***:** Iman Al Kouatly, Majeda Al-Ruzzieh, June Altaras, Rhonda Anderson, Sheila Antrim, Lori Armstrong, Margarita Baggett, Deb Baker, Claudia Garcia Barros, Kathy Barry, Dale Beatty, Sue Behrens, Rachel Behrendt, Christie Berner, Jenny Blank, Maureen Bowman, Anne Marie Brooks, Belinda Brown-Tezera, Shelly Buck, Karen Buckley, Michele Bunning, Linda Burnes-Bolton, Punjapon

Boonchua, Carol Bradley, Margo Bykonen, Laura Caramanica, Pam Cislo, Karen Clements, Connie Clemmons-Brown, Bonnie Clipper, Joyce Ramsey Coleman, Ric Cuming, Regina Cunningham, Sue Currin, Jim D'Alfonso, Janet Davis, Cindy Dawson, Ann Dechairo-Marino, Christie Dempsey, Bob Dent, Geraldine Dimalibot, Susie DiStefano, Mary Dixon, Kristine Donahue, Marilyn Dubree, Cole Edmonson, Lee Anne Eddy, Jane Englebright, Becky Enos, Linda Fahey, Christie Ferguson, Tysa Ferguson, Nanne Finis, Brenda Flynn, Debbie Ford, Mary Foley, Melissa Foreman-Lovell, Rhonda Foster, Carolyn Fox, Jayne Gmeiner, Gwen Gnam, Val Gokenbach, Eva Gomez, Colleen Goode, Miki Goodwin, Jennifer Graves, Karen Grimley, Kim Guesman, Mary Gullatte, Robin Hagenstad, Michael Hall, Beth Hammer, Kelly Hancock, Kathy Hardin, Janet Harris, Barry Hawthorne, Ann Hendrich, Karen Hill, Nancee Hofmeister, Linda Hunt, Lorraine Hughes, Diane Hupp, Judy Husted, Kelly Irving, Jeanette Ives-Erickson, Kelly Johnson, Kerry Jones, Helen King, Eileen Kingston, Chris Kowal, Gay Landstrom, Fran Laukaitis, Sandy Leake, Linda Leavell, Bill Lecher, Vickey Locey, Joan Loepker-Duncan, Holly Lorenz, Maricarmen Luhrsen, Craig Luzinski, Connie Ma, Louann Mace, Jerry Mansfield, Toby Marsh, David Marshall, Rick Martin, Veronica Martin, Laurel Mastro, Jody Mechanic, Meghan Mesa, Sheri Monsein, Martie Moore, Judy Moseley, Gladys Mouro, Liz Murphy, Sharon Pappas, Rosemarie O'Neill Paradis, Grace Parker, Marj Peck, Rosemary Perdue, Tammy Peterman, Pam Petto, Mary-Anne Ponti, Sandra Rader, Rosanne Raso, Elisa Reis, Janet Rice, Renee Roberts-Turner, Carol Robinson, Chris Ruder, Annette Russell, Kathy Sanford, Marlon Saria, Cindy Sayer, Marilyn Schaffner, Jineal Shinn, Gigi Siers, Rhonda Scott, Roy Simpson, Margie Sipe, Kathy Skowland, Eileen Sporing, Anne Stewart, Deirdre Stewart, Elaine Strachan-Hall, Michelle Stephenson, Jeffrey Stout, Mandie Sunderland, Nancy Susick, Jane Swanson, Linda Talley, Syl Trepanier, Paul Van Aken, Danny Van Heusden, Julie Ward, Noreen Watson, Paula Webb, Dickon Weir-Hughes, Ann Williamson, Susan Winslow, Laura Wood, Lamont Yoder, Anita Zuniga, and oh so many more—thank you! (Please don't hate us if we've left you out!)

Shining the Light on All the Right

✸ ✸ ✸

To our team present and past: A simple thank you seems insufficient. There is no way to adequately express our gratitude for you and your contributions.

Kate Ananson in Seattle: It's a joy to watch you in action as you manage your DAISY organizations. You ask the best questions, and your smile lights up every room you are in, even on video calls.

Jennifer Baldwin in California: We would be bankrupt without you as our bookkeeper, sending out thousands of invoices for everything from annual programs to a small bag of nominee pins.

Julie Blonk in Atlanta: You started out as a part-time program coordinator and have blossomed into an effective and creative full-time program manager.

Kara Ellis in Oklahoma City: Your growth from Christina's coordinator to a program director who represents DAISY beautifully has been a joy to behold.

Christina Johnson in Seattle: Your dedication to your region and to using technology to make us better at what we do is awesome.

Dana Love in Seattle: How do you do the job of editing the tens of thousands of DAISY Honorees' stories that are registered with us, uploading them to our website, and ensuring they're clear of privacy violations, while going through boxes of tissues to wipe away the tears they inspire?

Peter "Benedict" Maher in California: You are CFO Extraordinaire and Friend Extraordinaire, not to mention the best iPhone photographer of nurses and us ever.

Jaci Parks in Ohio: Watching you become an excellent program director and part of our DAISY family has been one of our many joys.

John Reynolds and Manuel Lopez in California: You ensure every box of DAISY gifts and every DAISY display that goes to the numerous conferences we attend are lovingly packed—and you somehow send everyone whatever they need on the day they're ordered and paid for.

Alexandra "Alex" Schoen in Ohio: We have been so fortunate to have your expertise and to have you travel with us. You are always comfortable engaging hospital leaders you've never met—and you always know where we've parked the car in a hospital parking lot.

Janet Silvestri in Michigan: You were the DAISY Coordinator at two of our hospitals when we asked you to join our then-tiny team, and the insights you gave us about running the program from the inside were invaluable—as you are today.

Cindy Sweeney in Maryland: You have truly amplified DAISY's voice and visibility with your presentations at nursing conferences on DAISY's behalf, thoughtful articles on meaningful recognition, including a column twice a year for the *Journal of Nursing Administration,* and more. You translate the language of nursing for all of us at DAISY. Thank you for being DAISY's Nurse and one of the world's great people-connectors.

To our DAISY Program Coordinators: Dawn Filipovitch, Lisa Flaherty, Meaghan Kapinos, Chelsea Moise, Nan Roderick, and Faith Thomas: You are linchpins of our communication to our DAISY community far and wide. Your management of SalesForce and attention to detail ensure we provide the level of service nurses deserve from us.

To those who have come and gone—Kathy Blount, Carol Bramlett, Amanda Dito, Peggy Gojcaj, Elysse Lane, Keisha Mwanganga, Kami Otis, Sheri Scholz, and Amy Vetter: Your contributions when you were with us were significant.

And finally to Erin Ascher: You joined us as an administrative assistant and have become so much more. You run our home; care for our two German shepherds, Max and Schultz, when we travel (in partnership with the best dog sitters ever, Kelly and Ken Woodle); and bring laughter and joy to our lives every day. We are so lucky that you are there with us and for us. Always.

Again, a sincere thank you to all of our team seems inadequate, but you all know how much we love you.

To our DAISY Supportive Associations: We owe you so much for spreading awareness and increasing the visibility of our work throughout the nursing profession, inviting us to bring DAISY to your conferences and to write for your journals.

Shining the Light on All the Right

The American Organization for Nursing Leadership (AONL) was first, when it was called AONE. In addition to Pam Thompson, we send our gratitude to Robyn Begley, Sue Gergely, Beverly Hancock, MT Meadows, and the numerous AONL board presidents who have embraced us: Laura Caramanica, Bob Dent, Linda Everett, Mary Ellen Fuchs, Donna Herrick, Cheryl Hoying, Michelle Janney, Mary Beth Kingston, Linda Knodel, Pam Rudisill, Maureen Swick, and Carol Watson.

The American Nurses Credentialing Center (ANCC) came next, bringing the DAISY Award to Magnet-designated organizations and then their Pathway to Excellence program. Thank you to every ANCC board and staff member who has embraced our work, especially Loressa Cole, Jeff Doucette, Karen Drenkard, Michael Evans, Jeanne Floyd, Rebecca Graystone, Debbie Hatmaker, Maureen Lal, Linda Lewis, Christine Pabico, Pat Reid-Ponte, and Marla Weston. Special shout-out to the wonderful Ellen "Boo" Lahman, who ensured that DAISY was always up front at every ANCC gathering.

At the American Nurses Association, ANCC's parent organization, we are grateful for the friendship of Pam Cipriano. Pam: As first vice president of the International Council of Nurses (ICN), you introduced us to the organization that is the voice of the world's 20 million nurses. Annette Kennedy: You opened the doors wide to ICN, providing a global showcase for our mission, and even introduced us personally to the director general of the World Health Organization, Dr. Tedros Adhanom. Thomas Kearns: As interim CEO of ICN at the time of our introduction, you became a tremendous ambassador, bringing DAISY with you when you returned to your position as executive director of the Royal College of Surgeons in Ireland's School of Nursing and Midwifery and the five hospitals with which it partners. Thanks to you, Thomas, we also enjoy the support of the European Nursing Council. And to Howard Catton, Thomas's successor at ICN: Thank you for being a gracious and welcoming leader.

To the American Association of Critical-Care Nurses (AACN): Thank you for your foundational work on meaningful recognition in nursing and for selecting us to receive your esteemed Pioneering Spirit

Award at your annual NTI (National Teaching Institute) conference in 2012. We have had a wonderful relationship ever since, thanks to the friendship of Connie Barden, Randy Bauler, Melinda Beckett-Maines, Linda Cassidy, Dorrie Fontaine, Wanda Johansson, Ramon Lavandero, Dana Woods, and so many members of AACN's board of directors over the years.

To the American Academy of Nursing: We were blown away when you inducted us as Honorary Fellows, thereby adding the credential FAAN to our names. Receiving this recognition on behalf of DAISY was unforgettable as Joanne Disch and Diana Mason honored us on stage and the audience stood to applaud our impact. Our sponsors for this surprise recognition were Mary Dee Hacker, Ruth Lindquist, and Roy Simpson. We truly have no words to describe our gratitude to you and the Academy for adding so much credibility and visibility to our work.

To Sigma Theta Tau International Honor Society of Nursing: You inducted us as Honorary Members in 2015 and celebrated DAISY with your Archon Award in 2019. We wear our Sigma pins proudly at all things DAISY, thanks to Ken Dion, Cindy Sweeney, Benson Wright, and others who supported us. Sigma's team, Kathy Bennison, Cathy Catrambone, Hester Klopper, Liz Madigan, Juli Maxworthy, Richard Ricciardi, Pat Thompson, and Beth Tigges were and are wonderful partners in driving meaningful recognition for nurses.

To the American Association of Colleges of Nursing (AACN): Your guidance and awareness building have been so valuable for the DAISY Faculty Award. Ann Carey, Robert Rosseter, Deb Trautman, and AACN board members: Thank you for issuing the national call to action for faculty recognition. It's having such positive results. The Organization of Associate Degree Nurses's Donna Meyer and the National League for Nursing's Janice Brewington and Beverly Malone have also supported the importance of recognition for faculty, as have numerous deans and faculty members who have befriended us and stood up for our mission, including Sharon Goldfarb, Cindy Greenberg, Susan Groenwald, Patty Hurn, Debra Jones, Victoria Rich, Anna Valdez, Ken White, Pat Yoder-Wise, and so many more.

To Melissa Fitzpatrick, then at Hill-Rom, and Patricia McGaffigan, at the National Patient Safety Foundation (now integrated into IHI, the Institute for Healthcare Improvement): You asked what we could do together to showcase the important role that nurses play in patient safety, and we created the DAISY Award for Extraordinary Nurses in Patient Safety. Hill-Rom has been the corporate sponsor for this award since its inception, and we are grateful that our partnership with IHI continues today through Patricia, Sabra Benedict, Kristi Cronin, Tejal Gandhi, and Pat McTiernan.

Finally, we owe our thanks to these nursing organizations that support DAISY with mutual marketing efforts. We are grateful to the leaders of each of these organizations for sharing our passion: Academy of Forensic Nursing, Academy of Medical-Surgical Nurses, American Academy of Ambulatory Care Nursing, American Association of Nurse Practitioners, American Assembly for Men in Nursing, Arkansas Association of Nurse Executives, Association of California Nurse Leaders, Association of Pediatric Hematology/Oncology Nurses, Association of periOperative Registered Nurses, Association for Nursing Professional Development, Canadian Association of Critical Care Nurses, Center for Nursing Foundation of New York State Nurses, Emergency Nurses Association, European Nursing Council, Hospice and Palliative Nurses Association, Institute for Healthcare Improvement, Institute for Patient- and Family-Centered Care, International Council of Nurses, International Transplant Nurses Society, Missouri Organization of Nurse Leaders, National Association of Directors of Nursing Administration (NADONA), National Nurses Association of Kenya, Navy Nurse Corps Association, Oncology Nursing Society, Philippine Nurses Association of America, Planetree International, Schwartz Center for Compassionate Healthcare, Sepsis Alliance, Society of Otorhinolaryngology and Head-Neck Nurses, Society of Pediatric Nurses, Society of Trauma Nurses, The Arnold P. Gold Foundation, and The Beryl Institute.

To the reviewers of the J. Patrick Barnes Grants for Nursing Research and Evidence-Based Practice Projects: You have spent untold hours carefully considering every submission, and we have learned so much listening in on your thoughtful deliberations about which work we should fund. Special heartfelt thanks to our panel chair since we started the program, Elizabeth Bridges: Your devotion to our mission to engage staff nurses in research demonstrates your focus on the future of nursing and healthcare. While Liz is on leave as the president-elect of the American Association of Critical-Care Nurses, Margaret Barton-Burke has taken over as chair. Margaret: You told us you wanted to volunteer with us—be careful what you wish for! DAISY and all our applicants are the beneficiaries of the very generous time and brainpower contributed by Liz, Margaret, and Kelly Brassil, Gina Bufe, Jean Ann Connor, Laura Cullen, Katherine Finn Davis, Kathleen Shannon Dorcy, Ann Dylis, Anna Gawlinski, Elise Arsenault Knudsen, Mary Beth Flynn Makic, Kathy Oman, and Patricia Thomas. We could not do this without you. Thank you all!

To the nurse-researchers: Your work has done so much from examining DAISY's impact on compassion fatigue and compassion satisfaction, to analyzing DAISY nomination stories to add depth and insight into how patients and families describe extraordinary nurses, and to providing qualitative research to understand what it means to patients and families to say thank you to nurses by nominating them for a DAISY Award. To Joanne Clavelle, Melissa Foreman-Lovell, Susan Grant, Senem Guney, Lesly Kelly, Cindy Lefton, Ellen Swartwout, Cindy Sweeney, and the many to come—thank you for your minds!

To the reviewers of DAISY's medical mission grant applications: We felt strongly that we needed to support our DAISY Nurses who want to share their compassion and skill with people who live where quality healthcare is scarce. You help make this possible. Thank you, Martha Abshire, Jose Arellano, Joanne Clavelle, Joanne Evans, Jill Glenn, Shellie Remenar, Kelly Thompson, and Nia Wright.

To the reviewers of DAISY's Cherokee Conference Scholarship program: As professional development budgets get smaller, you help our DAISY Nurses achieve their continuing drive for knowledge. Thank you, Stephanie Al-Adhami, Cindy Angiulo, Susan Bakewell, Regina

Coll, Sheri Cosme, Darleen Dagey, Patty Deasy, Marvin Delfin, Michele Healy, Laura Hendricks-Jackson, Irma Holland, Jennifer King, Denise Kishel, Cheryl Mallory, Mary Golway, Nancy Loos, Karen McCamant, Gewreka Nobles, Roxanne Sabatini, Chris Schumacher, Jean Shinners, Wendy Silverstein, Suzanne Taylor, and Amy Vetter.

❁ ❁ ❁

To everyone involved at our DAISY Breakfast at the Magnet Conference, sponsored by API Healthcare: We thought 75 people would accept our first invitation in 2014 to come have a Cinnabon before the conference's morning sessions started. We were stunned when 370 people accepted our invitation and that even more continue to do so five years later! But it wouldn't be nearly as special without our speakers each year.

Thank you, Maggie McClure: As one of the researchers who developed the basis for Magnet designation, we so appreciated your willingness to speak to—and captivate—the audience our first year. You made us know we could have a successful event each year.

Thank you, Susan Grant, Nancye Feistritzer, Sharon Vanairsdale, and Dustin Hillis for your riveting presentation in 2015 about treating the first Ebola patients to come to the United States at Emory University Hospital.

Thank you, Marie Manthey for your talk in 2016 about your life as a nurse and for telling us about your own nurse, Florence Marie Fisher. (Florence had been Marie's nurse when Marie had been hospitalized as a child and inspired her to become a nurse.) Together, we presented Florence with a posthumous DAISY Award, given to her son and granddaughter. Florence's granddaughter told us through tears that her grandmother never knew the impact she made as a nurse, simply by coloring in Marie's coloring book. What a perfect reinforcement of DAISY's mission.

Thank you, Tom and Kelley French: Your DAISY nomination was the first time you wrote about the NICU nurse who cared for your baby for 11 months. In 2017, you told your story that had become the book *Juniper: The Girl Who Was Born Too Soon.*

Thank you, Sue Hassmiller, Abby DiGaetano, and Kathy McLernan: Sue, there was much you could have talked about in 2018, but your words about tragically losing your husband, Bob, in a bicycle accident, and nominating Abby and Kathy, the two nurses who cared for you and Bob, were powerful. Abby and Kathy, we were thrilled you agreed to share your heartfelt story, too. We know how hard you all worked to prepare the presentation. Everyone in attendance was moved and grateful as well.

In 2019, we were asked to be the speakers at our DAISY Breakfast to celebrate our 20th anniversary. Sharing our gratitude to nurses who have guided us over the last two decades to make DAISY what it is today made us even more appreciative of the all of the speakers who came before us and reinforced the tremendous gratitude we have for them. We will never forget your most wonderful presentations to members of the DAISY Community.

To our generous donors and supporters who helped us establish DAISY, especially in the early days: Artie Marino, the late Tom Martin, Richard Schaps, David Yacullo, and Lamar Outdoor (Patrick's employer in Amarillo), you were Patrick's and our business colleagues in the advertising and billboard business and got us started with generous contributions in his memory—thank you! Bob and Yphon LaRoche (Tena and Pat's neighbors in Amarillo): You were so helpful when we started DAISY. Carolyn and Matt Wood: Thank you for never letting a Christmas go by without a generous donation to our mission. Bill Clark, Diane Frankel, Donna and Ed Horner, Patrick Lynch, Stacy and Dave Parks, and Charlie White: Thank you for keeping DAISY on your list of donations, always believing in what we do, and being so tolerant of all the times DAISY kept us from being around.

To our Industry Partners: Thank you for sharing our passion for nurses and developing such mutually beneficial relationships.

To Cinnabon: Your delicious cinnamon rolls have been a part of DAISY celebrations since the beginning—you have donated more than one million cinnamon rolls to nurses! Jennifer Dempsey and Geoff Hill, our gratitude for creating our relationship is profound. Extra thanks to you, Jennifer, for getting Kerry Foods to donate jars of Cinnabon cinnamon to those hospitals that didn't have a bakery nearby. Thank you also to the many executives at Cinnabon who have sustained our partnership over the years, including Kat Cole, Loryn Franco, Joe Guith, Kristen Hartman, Debbie Rowley, and Lucy Weyand. And thank you to the company's franchise partners with a special salute to the creator of the world's best cinnamon roll, Jerilyn Brusseau.

To GetWellNetwork (Industry Partner since 2008): When Connie Clemmons-Brown asked if she could accept DAISY Award nominations via your network, we had never heard of your technology that helps patients become more engaged in their own care. So Connie introduced us. Mike Schram: You understood the value of our mission immediately and made it possible for patients in hospitals that used the technology to nominate their nurses through the system. You also introduced us to Michael O'Neil, who created the company out of his personal experience with healthcare as a young man with lymphoma who had no control over his own care and never wanted others to feel the same way. Michael: You served on our board and brought a great perspective and view of our future, not to mention a wonderful spirit, to every meeting and interaction. In addition, the warmth and support of every member of your team has made working with them a joy. Thank you, Laura Bramschreiber, Kenny Brooks, Leah Bruch, Joanne Clavelle, Tony Cook, Ellie Corso, Karen Drenkard, Katie Edge, Scott Filion, Nate Fletcher, Abry Garfoot, Bill Gilroy, Taryn Habberey, Leah Hackmann, Paula Hamm, Heather Hayes, Erick Holliday, David Jack, Sean Lara, TR Lind, Mike Moore, Holly Murphy, Joe Nora, Shannon O'Neil, Wendy O'Neil, Joe Rockland, Jodi Smith, Wanda Stoner, Wendy Strait, and Chelcy Walczy. And to David Wright: You may not get the spotlight that Michael O'Neil gets, but we so appreciate all you do for DAISY behind the scenes.

To Hill-Rom (Industry Partner since 2008): Our relationship began thanks to the vision of Melissa Fitzpatrick who worked for you at the time. Today, our relationship with you has been enriched by the many people who have engaged with DAISY in the past and today: Joanne Anderson, Jason Bill, Dan Chaplick, Dan Cheever, Mark Delaney, Rossana Fernandez, Dan Ferris, Scott Hoerner, Dee Kumbar, Marlene Meister, Teri Nobbe, Kevin Moore, Ernesto Pirrotta, Michael Ramsey, Jodi Raynor, Jim Sewell, Alton Shader, Lindsay Sloan, Barry Smith, Patty Tomlinson, Carlos Urrea, Pete Wick, and Pete Zawodniak. We are excited about the outcomes we describe together as you provide technology that helps nurses to be DAISY-worthy nurses.

To Cherokee Medical Uniforms (Industry Partner since 2010): Mike Singer, you have chosen the DAISY Foundation as one of the ways to express your dedication to the profession and seemingly can't do enough to support nurses—thank you. We also deeply appreciate the amazing team at Cherokee and its parent company, Strategic Partners, Inc. (SPI), and at Scrubsmag.com for your partnership. Thanks to SPI, we have a beautiful and moving new web video, Cherokee Nursing Conference Scholarships for our honorees, Cherokee "DAISY Wear" for our Honorees and DAISY Committees, distribution of this book, and so much more. And thank you to our partners behind the scenes at SPI, including Mike Alexander, Michael Harbron, Lisa Hatfield, Kay Heitzman, Stephanie Kraus, Wendell Mobley, Renata Ritcheson, David Silverman, Debbie Singer, Phil Suarez, Kim Webb, and Caroline Zelonka.

To API Healthcare (Industry Partner since 2012): Karlene Kerfoot and Kathy Douglas, you brought us to the attention of J.P. Fingado, who understood our mission and how partnering with DAISY might serve us both. That led to API's sponsorship of our DAISY Breakfast at the Magnet Conference since 2014. Karlene and Patti Dorgan: The book of nurses' notes about DAISY you gave us at the 2019 breakfast was an unbelievable gift; every note touched us deeply. It's a joy to work with you and to partner with the API and symplr team, past and present, that works with us and joins us when we travel. Thank you Eric Bauer, Joanna Bendarzewski, Pamela Bonnett, Chris Bowler, Wayne Canner, Collette Cleary, Patti Dorgan, Lois Evans, Mary Farmand, Jody Fitts, Brian Fugere, Jeff Gal, Charles Haibel, Christine Hoxworth, Robert Jacobs, Richard Jordan, Jennifer Kraier, Lisa LaBau, Dottie Lutz, Pete

Mattocks, Tracey Meyer, Cindy Miller, Michele Morin, Sarah Neis, Corey Pachciarz, Courtney Pattee, Kim Peters, Rick Pleczko, Rachel Pledger, Randall Pruitt, Ramiro Roman, Jeff Rupprecht, Joe Soldovieri, Kalli Sutton, Barbara Tannenbaum, Brian Van Bloom, Julie Walker, Rosanne Wassom, and Mike Wingert. Special thanks to Daryl Joslin: Your marketing work for API impressed us so much that when you left, we asked you to consult with DAISY. Thank you for being a trusted advisor to DAISY, not to mention a great friend, eating and drinking DAISY every day with us!

To Chamberlain University (Industry Partner since 2013): Peggy Guillory, you started what we know will be a lifelong friendship when you told us that you had gone to meet with Stuart Downs and found his office filled with DAISY goodies for a DAISY Award presentation to one of his nurses. You called us shortly after the presentation to ask about sponsorship opportunities and enlisted your colleague Ken Malito, knowing that his engagement would really help ensure a partnership would ensue. The result today is every DAISY Honoree is entitled to a reduction in tuition at Chamberlain, and the faculty and students are recognized with the DAISY Award. Big thanks to you and to all at Chamberlain who make a difference for DAISY: David Blackburn, Mary Collins, Karen Cox, Carole Eldridge, Bart Fitz, Susan Groenwald, Jason Henrikson, Ranil Herath, Taryn Hill, Linda Hollinger-Smith, Tonya Kimber-Jones, Walter Kowalczyk, Kristie Marino, Latrease Purnell, Jill Price, Kory Robison, Karilyn Van Oosten, and the army of healthcare development specialists who travel with our staff to DAISY presentations and even attend on their own, a fresh bouquet of daisies at the ready for the Honoree of the day.

To Kirby Bates Associates (KBA, Industry Partner since 2013): Karen Kirby, you not only were the first of our industry partners to put our DAISY Partner logo in your email signature, but are a wonderful friend who trooped around the country visiting hospitals with us. You welcome visitors to KBA's booth at conferences with a sticker indicating that you made a donation to DAISY in honor of their visit. When you were not available for trooping, members of your team made wonderful contributions to our visits: Lorrie Anderson,

Pam DeCampli, Jane Fitzsimmons, Jennifer Insua, Peggy Loughery, and Doris Sinkevich. Now that Jackson Healthcare owns KBA, we are also grateful for the support of Scott L'Heureux and KBA's new leader, Melissa Fitzpatrick.

To Versant Holdings (Industry Partner since 2013): Michael Carman, when you heard us speak at your client conference for the first time, you had tears in your eyes when you said to us afterwards, "We have to talk about how we can support DAISY." The synergy in our missions was apparent, and we couldn't be more grateful for our partnership. You and Larissa Africa even invited us to join your Versant Advisory Council (quite an honor). It's a privilege to have you among our esteemed Industry Partners, and we thank Mike and Larissa, as well as Tammy Franqueiro, Betsy Rudolph, Jean Shinners, and the rest of the Versant team.

To Medtronic (Industry Partner since 2016): Patty Reilly, from the moment Ann Evans introduced us, you wanted to help and navigated your way through the complex Medtronic system, with the help of Doug Bartlett whose devotion to nurses was tangible. It wasn't long before you instructed us on how to apply for a grant from Medtronic, and the company joined our roster of Industry Partners. Your team members are great traveling partners who love attending DAISY celebrations so they stay connected to the real work of the people who use their devices and products—nurses. Thank you, Michael Beglin, Brett Belokin, Russ Bird, Gina Farquharson, Erich Faust, David Giarracco, John Guarino, Kris Kovel, Bill McGarry, Jeff McIntosh, Tracy McQuay, George Mullen, Eddie Perez, Robert St. John, Mike Stevenson, and especially to Mini Szasz, grant coordinator.

And finally to HealthcareSource (Industry Partner since 2018): When J.P. Fingado left API, he joined HealthcareSource and introduced DAISY to his new team. In a short time, the company has let nurse leaders know of your support for DAISY, and by extension all nurses, by distributing pens in the shape of a daisy in a pot. It's a kick to see the line of nurse leaders at the HealthcareSource booth wanting to talk to your staff and pick up their DAISY pens. Thank you to Sean Parlin, Kelli Rice, Alison Ryberg, Katherine Shuman, Russ Wakelin, Dave Wilkins, Denise Zeidman, and the ever-so-creative Alena Zelem.

To those who gave financial support to our partner hospitals and organizations: Posthumous thanks to: Carl Lindner Jr., former owner of the Cincinnati Reds, whom we never met but who sponsored several of our hospitals in Cincinnati and gave every nurse in the area two tickets to a game every summer; and to the late Stephen Weiss, who generously underwrote our program at NewYork-Presbyterian Weill Cornell Medical Center where he was on the board of trustees and was a recipient of the nurses' excellent care.

Sharman Lamka: Your support for the hospitals that cared for your beloved husband, Phil, is a gift! So is the recognition you named in his memory to honor respiratory therapists.

When Wright Lassiter III was at Alameda Health System, honoring nurses was so important to you that you personally sponsored the program for your staff. Now that you're at Henry Ford Health, we are very proud of your ongoing friendship.

Tyler Mason at UnitedHealth Group: You sponsored the first year of DAISY at over 100 hospitals. You also appointed a public relations consultant, Anita Sen, to set up media events at each one to help make the hospitals' communities aware of the excellent nursing available at each DAISY facility you sponsored. And your introduction to David Hansen and other regional executives who participated in these events added to the honor given to nurses. Thank you, Tyler, David, Anita, and all at UnitedHealth Group who have touched our program.

For many years, Wells Fargo supported our mission thanks to Jonathan Weedman. Jon: You arranged for funding for seven DAISY hospitals in the Los Angeles area. Your associate Jack Toan liked the concept so much that he too funded a hospital in Orange County. Thank you both.

Individuals who supported hospitals in the early years and even today also include the late Mary Gloisten, Donna and Ed Horner, Jay Jensen of NovaVine, Norma and Fred Lipman, and Barbara Murdock-Perra. Thank you all!

To the companies and people that have helped ensure that we serve our DAISY community well: Kim Hofmann: As a SalesForce consultant, you made our use of the system so much better. We only wish we could have afforded to hire you when SalesForce first donated the platform to us. Thank you, SalesForce and Kim!

Suzanne Allen: You helped us acquire DAISY pins, lanyards, and other promotional items in the early years. Ken Scholz: You took that business to a whole new level for us. Kevin Jones and Shawn Morris of FastSigns of Santa Rosa: You produce our banners and signs so beautifully, and your service is truly excellent. Amber Waddle of Hall's Executive Gifts: Our hospital partners appreciate the plaques and pins you produce for us. Dennis Vaughan: You have been supplying our handsome DAISY Award certificate portfolios since our board member Mark Kamstra suggested they would make a more professional presentation than the frames we were buying at Costco. Chris Loxton of Loxton Cellars: You are not just a friend and neighbor but you make the extra special gift of our DAISY Block Syrah for our volunteer board members and various nursing functions. Thank you all for what you do so wonderfully!

MIX Branding and Strategy in Southern California: You took DAISY on as a pro bono client in 2008 and have been doing our graphics almost forever. Phil Buck: Thank you for creating our branding, brochures, and marketing materials for our participating hospitals. In 2014, when it was time for a whole new look and feel for DAISY, we even became a paying agency client and our loyalty to you, Phil, and to Mollie McDonough runs deep as ever.

Mike Soden of Harcalf Agency and Bryan Fogelman of NetEasy: You designed and managed our first website—you put our voice on the internet! When the site became very complex, we started working with an agency in downtown Glen Ellen, our hometown: A. Bright Idea. Designer Brian Lobsinger, thank you for being a genius and a delight to work with.

Thank you, O.R. Nurses Nationwide: You were the first staffing agency to bring the DAISY Award to traveling nurses, thanks to the vision of your founder, Denise Stewart. You have been a great partner and very generous financially. AMN Healthcare: Thank you for attracting visitors to your conference booths by offering a donation to DAISY. Cerner Corporation: You were the first company to honor your extensive international nursing staff, thanks to the innovation of Roy Simpson. (Yes, Roy, Scotch does taste better when it's drunk out of a crystal glass!) Special thanks to Toni Bennett, Patience Chinwadzimba, Jenny Horn, Eva Karp, Gail Latimer, Matt Pickett, Mike Pomerance, Distie Profit, and Deirdre Stewart.

Years ago, we asked Susan Grant if she happened to know anyone at Kimberly-Clark who could supply Kleenex packs for our DAISY presentations. The ceremonies are often so emotional, and the nurses search for tissues. Thank you, Susan, for putting us in touch with Jay Hexamer from Kimberly-Clark. A few weeks later, the pallet of Kleenex packs that arrived at our home was a great surprise. Thank you, Jay! When you left the company, we so appreciated that Dave Parks, your successor, continued the tradition for years, along with Michele Curtis, Alex Hodges, Chris Sloan, Lon Taylor, Quincy Witherspoon, and Krista Zanine. Thank you for absorbing so many tears.

Nurse.com: Thank you for being a great supporter of DAISY's mission. Heather Cygan, Sallie Jimenez, and Robert Hess (now retired) have created a beautiful digital guide to all things DAISY and a significant web-based resource to share what we do and how we do it.

Joe Tye of Values Coach, Inc.: Thank you for never failing to mention the DAISY Award as you embed positivity in healthcare cultures around the country. Thanks also for the two enormous pens you sent to get us started on this book. Seeing you and Michelle Arduser is always uplifting. You are a true friend to us both.

Creative Health Care Management's work and DAISY's mission have great synergy. We love our frequent conversations with Mary Koloroutis with whom we wrote our first white paper. Thank you!

As we have endeavored to ensure easy access for patients and families to nominate their nurses, looking for electronic means of submitting nominations and tracking them has become a priority. We are grateful to you, Rohan Walvekar and Bryan Phou, for creating a beautiful platform for DAISY digital nominations, powered by your system, nDorse. And to you, CJ Floros and Tom Hills, for your inclusion of DAISY in your nurse manager solution, Laudio. As these two technologies move into the market, we wish you wild success!

One more special thank you to these special people: Racha Abou, Gordon Blumenfeld, Lindsay Bowles, Sandie Carlson, Sara Caven, Helen Cortopassi, Paula Cox, Christie DiMichele, Gabrielle Fortaleza, Chuck Gayton, Enrique Geronimo, Lindsay Hong, Josh Lawson, Karla Mavity, Maya Nizam, Sarah Perron, Nichole Rodgers, Shirley Ryan, Ann Ryder (who taught us to never follow a TV news anchor and accomplished speaker on the stage of a conference), Josh Sokoloff, Jennifer Speth, Carrie Svendsen, Cristina Suarez, Toni Tucker, Jean Weber, and Peter Wright.

※ ※ ※

Who have we left out?

To our SOBS (Spouses of the Board and Staff): You come to Sonoma once a year for a multiday retreat. It's tough work visiting Sonoma wineries and craft breweries while our hard-working board meets, but someone has to—and you are all so good at it! Thank you to the people and places who have hosted our board and SOBS' dinners: St. Anne's Crossing (the winery that buys our Primitivo grapes), Suzy and Squire Fridell, the late Joe and Jann Capone, Balletto Winery, and LaRochelle Winery—always catered by our friend Catherine Venturini of Cuvee Wine Country Events. Thank you, Catherine and Stephanie! And thanks to Sondra Bernstein who hosted us for board dinners and donated meals to nurses in our early years.

This may sound strange, but we also must acknowledge our insurance company for DAISY, the Hartford Company. The responsiveness of adjuster Greg Gatewood and speed of payment for our loss from the fire was remarkable. Greg, we'll never forget when you came to visit and stood by the burn pile that had once been DAISY's shipping office, big tears in your eyes as you saw our loss.

Finally, we have so many personal friends who stand by us as we dedicate our lives to DAISY, knowing we are often not home or available for social activities. But you are always interested in what we are doing for nurses and caring that we are healthy and happy. Lauri and Tim Dorman, Angie and Nick Frey, Val and the late Jerry Gibbons, Joan and the late Jim Griffin, Bonnie and the late Henry Lasky, Joanie and Bob Lipman, Jamie and TeeJay Lowe, Dennis McLeod and David Armario, Vicki and Paul Michalcyzk, Anna and Frank Pope, Gerry and Corinne Simpson, and Sandy Zuckerman and her wonderful late husband, Ira (who was with us for our first "aggressive discussion"). And thanks to three people who have taken incredibly good care of us and our home for all these years: Cindy Hoffman, Mindy Johnson, and Teresa Rodriguez.

Thank you for being so wonderful and understanding, all of you.

And last but always first in our hearts . . . the nurses who have embraced, enhanced, and even built DAISY by telling each other about it and taking it from one organization to another.

To the hundreds of thousands of nurses who have been honored with the DAISY Award: We hope we helped you understand that by "just doing your job" you made a lasting impression on your patients.

To all the nurses who have been nominated: Please treasure the fact that people took the time to share stories of their care with you.

To the tens of thousands of DAISY Coordinators, committee members, and administrative assistants: The DAISY Award comes to life with your dedication of time, creativity, resourcefulness, and passion for our mission.

To every CNO and CNE (the whole c-suite, for that matter) who understands, values, and supports meaningful recognition of nurses: You have shone the light on all the right.

You all have our undying gratitude. This story is yours as much as it is ours. We just want to say thank you, one more time. To all of you.

And to Our Patrick.

Index

Pages in *italics* are photographs. For names not listed and for more citations of listed names, see pages 171–193

A
Adventist Feather River Hospital, 124
Al Amro, Abdullah, 104–105

Alta Bates Hospital, 44
America West Airlines, 41, 42
American Academy of Nursing, 151, 152
American Association for Nursing Development, 89
American Association of Colleges of Nursing (AACN), 128

American Association of Critical-Care Nurses (AACN), 64, 134–135

American Nurses Credentialing Center (ANCC), 100–101, 102, 107, 142, 151, *151*

American Organization for Nursing Leadership (AONL). *See* American Organization of Nurse Executives

American Organization of Nurse Executives (AONE), 46, 64, 88–93, 102, 111, 122, 135

American University Medical Center (Beirut), 102

Angiulo, Cindy, 29, 30, 32, 88, 120

Antoku, Marion, 62, 63

Ascher, Erin, 164, 165

"Auntie Bonkers." *See* Barnes, Melissa

B

Bacon, Angela, 25

Baptist Saint Anthony Medical Center, 4, 8, 39

Barnes, Adam, 8, 113

Barnes, Bonnie and Mark, *32*, *103*, *106*, *115*, *151*
   inseparability, 152, 156

Barnes, Brad, 8

Barnes, Dianne, 8, 14, 20, 26, 29–30, 31, 41, 87, 120, 135

Barnes, J. Patrick, *15*, *79*
   early life, 4, 6, 121
   illness with ITP, 3–5, 7–14
   nurses' care for, 7–8, 9, 10–11, 21–22, 150, 156
   "Our Patrick", 5, 6, 7, 13, 20, 83, 92, 107, 115, 150, 157

positive character, 6, 7, 9, 11, 14, 21, 27, 28, 78, 79, 80

Barnes, Melissa, 107, 113–114, 115, *115*

Barnes Carraher, Riley, 3–4, 6, 11, 14, *15*, 26, 75, 78, *79*, *106*, 109, 110, 172

Barnes Carraher, Tena, 11–14, 21 26, 75, 88, 109–111, 112, 114, *115*
   naming DAISY, 20, 22
   nurses' consideration for, 11–12, 21–22

Behrendt, Rachel, 123, 124

Bridges, Elizabeth, 121

Bronson Methodist Hospital, 154

Bumrungrad International Hospital (Bangkok), 105

C

Caramanica, Laura, 135, 136

Carraher, John, 110, 111

Carraher, Riley Barnes. *See* Barnes Carraher, Riley

Carraher, Tena. *See* Barnes Carraher, Tena

Cedars-Sinai Medical Center, 39, 82

Center for Psychiatry, Winter Haven Hospital, 94

Chamberlain University, 128, 142

Children's Hospital Cincinnati, *73*

Children's Hospital Los Angeles, 60–61, 62, 63, 64, 65, 78

Children's Hospital Oakland, 44

Cinnabon, 7, 8, 42–43, 100, 110, 123, 158

Coffman, Lisa, 62, 63

Crome, Patti, 88

Crow, Greg, 105–106

D

D'Aquila, Richard, 40

DAISY Award. *See also specific awards*
  banner, 72, *73*, 81, 93, 120
  certificate, 23, 28, 31, 50, 52, 76, 93
  criteria for, 31, 32, 72, 80. *See also* nomination process
  first presentation, 31–32, *32*
  gifts, 23, 27, 28, 29, 30, 31, 37, 38, 43, 45, 46, 49–50, 52, 61, 72, 74, 76, 112, 119, 120, 130. *See also* Cinnabon; *Healer's Touch* sculpture; pin
  growth of, 34, 38–40, 61, 63, 64–67, 80, 81, 82, 93, 100, 102, 107, 111, 112–113, 150–151
  impact on nurses, 25, 37, 45, 49, 59, 71, 74, 75–76, 78, 87, 99, 119, 122, 127, 130, 133, 138–142, 149, 155
  impact on organizations, 33, 44, 45, 61, 63, 65–66, 74, 75, 80–81, 89–90, 93, 107, 109, 112, 125, 126, 138–142
  initial ideas for, 21–23, 27–28, 29–30
  internationalism, 100–107
  limits on, 125–126
  nomination process, 29, 31, 32, 33, 46, 63, 66, 72, 74, 75–76, 80, 81, 105, 114
  nurses' acceptance of concept, 28, 32, 75, 78–79
  nurses' expansion of concept, 72–74, 78–79, 119–130, 152, *153*
  pin, 23, 28, 37, 50, 52, 72, 74, 112, 120, 130
  reach of, 130, 150
  research on impact of, 134–142
  scrapbooks, 78, 79, 165

DAISY Award for Extraordinary Nursing Students, 129

DAISY Champion recognition, 126–127

"DAISY Dust," 43

DAISY Faculty Award, 65, 127–129

DAISY Foundation
  awards and recognition for, 106, 144, *151*, 151–152, 167
  board members, 43, 44, 63, 64, 65, 67, 87–88, 110, 115, 116, 120, 121, 125, 127, 150, 167. *See also individual names;* 171–193
  corporate sponsors, 41, 42, 64, 81, 82. *See also specific companies;* 171–193
  database, 67, 83, 91
  funding by, 27, 120–121
  funding of, 23, 26, 41, 64, 80, 81–83, 87–88, 91, 92–93
  initial ideas for, 20, 22–23, 26–27, 45
  naming, 20
  newsletter, 41, 78, 79
  operations, 55, 67, 111, 112, 113–116, 136, 164
  research grants, 120–121
  website, 44, 72, 78, 114

DAISY Founders' Coin, 126

DAISY Lifetime Achievement Award, 129, 130

DAISY Medical Mission Grants, 121

DAISY Model of Impact, 142–143, *143*

DAISY Nurse Leader Award, 122, 127

DAISY Team Award, *123*, 123–125

Dan (nurse in Amarillo), 7, 21

Dechairo-Marino, Ann, 45, 46, 61

Dempsey, Jennifer, 43

Doll, Lynne, 39, 82, 121

Duerksen, Christine, 99

E

Edwards, Debbie Zahren, 59

Emergency Department, Bethesda Hospital West, 131

England, Judy and Bruce, 39

Evans, Ann, 63–64, 88

F

Fiddler, John, 40–41

Fitzpatrick, Melissa, 42

Floyd, Jeanne, 100–101

Foreman-Lovell, Melissa, 142

Fred Hutchinson Cancer Research Center, 8, 9, 14, 20, 21, 28, 29, 30

G

George, Dr. James, 8, 26

George, Jisha, 108

Gergely, Sue, 90, 91

Godfrey, Cynthia, 40

Grady Memorial Hospital, 154

Grant, Susan, 29, 33, 65, 66, 75, 142

Griffin, Joan and Jim, 164

Groenwald, Susan, 128, 142

H

Hacker, Mary Dee, 60–62, 63, 64–65, 88, 125

Hartzog, Meredith, 119

Healer's Touch sculpture, 46, 49–52, *51*, *54*, 55–56, 119, 129, 130, 165, *166*, 167. See also *Mother and Child*

Health Alliance of Greater Cincinnati, 65

Heyman, Beth, 65, 88, 127

Hill, Geoff, 43

Hilliard, Donna, 102, 103, 104

Hill-Rom, 42

Horton, Joan, 84

Hospice of the Valley, 41, 42

Hospital for Sick Children (Toronto), 102

Hospital Israelita Albert Einstein (São Paulo), 105

Hurn, Patty, 127, 128

I

Idiopathic thrombocytopenic purpura. *See* ITP

Impact Model, DAISY, 142–143, *143*

Intensive Care Unit Team, Southern New Hampshire Medical Center ICU, 35

International Council of Nursing, 107

ITP, 3–5, 7–8, 10, 13

Support Association, 27

supporting research to treat and cure, 20, 23, 26–27, 78, 79, 120

J

J. Patrick Barnes Grants for
    Nursing Research and Evidence-
    Based Practice Projects, 120–121
Johnson & Johnson, 41
Johnson, Rebecca, 71

K

Kamstra, Jane, 88
Karen (nurse in Seattle), 12–13, 21
Kearns, Thomas, 144
Kelly, Lesly, 141, 142
Kessler, Nikole, 145
King Fahad Medical City, 102,
    104–105
King Faisal Specialist Hospital and
    Research Centre, 100, 101, 102,
    103, 108
Koloroutis, Mary, 143

L

Lasky, Bonnie, 43–44, 60, 88
Lefton, Cindy, 135–141, 142
Levine, Susan Goldwater, 41–42
Lovering, Sandy and Craig, 100
Lower Keys Medical Center, 154
Lynne Doll Grants for
    Dissemination of Findings, 121

M

Magill, Jennifer, 19
Magnet Recognition Program®, 34,
    65–66, 80, 100–101, 102, 116,
    116, 151, 151
Maher, Peter, 106, 115–116
Mantundan, Dana, 117
Marzullo, Donna, 68
McClellan, Laura, 142
Meadows, MT, 90, 91

Memorial Sloan Kettering Cancer
    Center, 78
Mercy San Juan Medical Center,
    78, 79
Morton Plant Mease Health Care,
    153
Moseley, Judy, 101–102
Mother and Child sculpture, 50–52,
    53, 54
Mowatt, Megan, 37

N

NewYork-Presbyterian Weill
    Cornell Medical Center, 40
Northampton General Hospital
    (England), 105
Northridge Medical Center, 45
Nottingham University Hospitals
    NHS Trust, 105, 106
Nurse recognition program. See
    DAISY Award

O

Oncology Team Snow Day, UCLA
    Medical Center Santa Monica,
    56
Opseth, Greg, 87
Organization of Associate Degree
    Nurses, 128
OSF Saint Francis Medical Center,
    74

P

Pakieser-Reed, Katherine, 149
Piedmont Hospital, 110
Platelet Disorder Support
    Association, 27
Providence St. Vincent's Hospital,
    72, 73

R

Renown Health. *See* Washoe
  Medical Center
Reynolds, John, 53–56, 67, 111
Rice, Janet, 129
Riley Children's Hospital, 110
Robert (nurse in Amarillo), 9
Robinson, Carol, 44
Robinson, Michele, 49
Royal College of Surgeons School
  of Nursing and Midwifery
  (Dublin), 144

S

SalesForce, 91, 113, 114
San Francisco General Hospital, 44,
  78, 106
Santa Rosa Memorial Hospital, 39,
  52
Saudi Arabia, 99–105, 107
Schmit, Rebecca, 23
Schoen, Alex, 150
Scott, Rhonda, 154
Seattle Cancer Care Alliance, 28,
  29–33, 34
Shangrove, Kenna Smith, 31–32, *32*
Shive, Katherine, 158
Sigma Theta Tau International
  Honor Society of Nursing, 107,
  151
Sipe, Margie, 133
Sonoma Valley Hospital, 39, 52
Stewart, Deidre, 102
Stormer, Carolyn, 31–32
Surgical Care Unit at Children's
  National Medical Center, *123*
Swaim, Jane, 71–72
Sweeney, Cindy, 142–143

T

Tana (nurse in Seattle), 12, 21, 133
Thomas Jefferson University
  Methodist Hospital, 123, 153
Thompson, Pam, 88, 89–93
Trautman, Deb, 128
Turme, Steve, 39

U

UnitedHealthcare, 82
University of Iowa Hospitals and
  Clinics, 129
University of Washington (UW)
  Medical Center, 28–33, 34, 39,
  65, 88, 110, 120
USAir. *See* America West

V

Vogus, Timothy, 142

W

Wain, Bea, 59–60
Washoe Medical Center, 39
Weedman, Jonathan, 64
Wells Fargo Foundation, 64
Westchester Medical Center, 135
Williford, Justin, 47
Wilshaw, Jane, 104

Y

Young, Donna, 109